GUIDE TO
GEOLOGIC LITERATURE

GUIDE TO
GEOLOGIC LITERATURE

RICHARD M. PEARL
Colorado College
Colorado Springs, Colorado

FIRST EDITION

McGRAW-HILL BOOK COMPANY, INC.

NEW YORK   TORONTO   LONDON

1951

GUIDE TO GEOLOGIC LITERATURE

Dedicated to

Theophania H. Crawford

and

R. D. Crawford

1873–1950

Professor of Mineralogy, University of Colorado

who "imported into Education the wisdom of life.
... By simple living, by an illimitable soul, you
inspired, you corrected, you instructed, you raised,
you embellished all."—*Emerson*

PREFACE

The growing importance of geology in these early days of atomic technology seems enough justification for this guidebook to the literature of geology, its subdivisions, and its related fields. Because of the close relationship of applied geology to the fast-expanding fields of engineering, geology is, along with the other sciences, occupying more attention in schools and industry than heretofore. Geologic publications can be expected to keep pace with the increased employment in geologic work and the greatly increased number of college and university students majoring in geologic studies.

Becoming acquainted with the literature is a considerable part of the lifetime work of any progressive geologist, who must, as Newton said of himself, stand on giants' shoulders in order to see farther. The rediscovery of already published facts is a tragic waste of time and energy. "The library habit is utterly essential to sound scientific research . . . and geologists who do not know how to prepare acceptable reports are not quite ready for professional status," say the men who wrote *Training Geologists: A United States Geological Survey Viewpoint*, adding that students should "know how to use geologic literature as an instrument of research." With the guidance that the author hopes this book will furnish, they can acquire in a systematic way this invaluable technique of searching the literature, and do so more readily than in the usual haphazard manner of developing such skills. This has been accomplished successfully in other subjects, notably chemistry. Students in this field have been well served by books by such authors as Soule, Mellon, and Crane and Patterson, from each of whom the author has secured information and inspiration. Similar books are available in geography, biology, mathematics, physics, and engineering.

The voluminous nature of the scientific literature makes such guides necessary; otherwise students and even active practitioners may flounder in the vast morass of printed matter. The literature of geology is more difficult than that of many other subjects because of the confusing complexity of much of its source material, as is brought out in the first chapter.

Effort has been made to cover, by means of appropriate references to lists, indexes, and bibliographies, all published literature on geology from the earliest dates (even though now quite obsolete), as well as current material of vital significance to present discoveries and developments. In its scope the book is designed to serve both the history-minded student and the practicing geologist. The problems of the geologist are emphasized rather than those of the librarian, but the subject matter should be useful to the latter also.

Several directories intended to be of value are presented, including those of the state geologic surveys, bureaus of mines, agricultural experiment stations, and the geologic surveys of all the nations of the world. These lists either have not been published before or else they contain at least some new information.

Details as to the availability of the literature are given wherever possible so that those interested in obtaining certain publications or in building up a library may know how to secure them by purchase or free distribution.

Where a publication may properly be considered in more than one place, it is discussed at length in the chapter to which it is most essential and is merely referred to elsewhere.

An American emphasis is inevitable, as domestic material is more accessible and more familiar to the author, but a sincere effort has been made to include as much outside literature as possible.

This book deals first with general material and then proceeds to more specific topics. Part I is an introductory section outlining the problems and peculiarities of geologic literature and furnishing a survey of the entire field as an over-all guide to the rest of the book. Part II discusses library facilities and methods involved in the use of all the kinds of geologic literature that are considered in Part III. It also contains a chapter on indexing, because any of the various types of publication may contain its own index, though perhaps issued separately. Part III, the largest section of the book, begins with a chapter on general index guides and bibliographies, discusses in succeeding chapters thirteen types of literature, including unpublished material, and closes with a chapter on maps. The author has placed these chapters in what he believes to be a logical and satisfactory sequence, and one that the reader might employ in an exhaustive search of the literature involving an entirely new problem. Other approaches may, of course, be preferable, depending upon the nature of the problem, the facilities at hand, and the experience of the individual. These are discussed in Chapter 2 on Conducting the Search.

Part III begins (Chapter 7) with the most general and least detailed kind of guide to geologic literature—indexes and bibliographies, which are fundamentally lists of references. Annotated and summarized lists of references are called "abstracts"; these, discussed in Chapter 8, present more detailed information about the literature described in later chapters. The chapter on periodicals (Chapter 9) treats original and independent publications, which are sometimes incorporated into more extensive and permanent presentations in bulletins (Chapters 10 to 14) or books (Chapter 15). Chapters 10 to 14 deal with five kinds of bulletins which are arranged in the following order: (1) Federal documents of the United States, (2) publications of institutions of national scope, some of which are of semiofficial status, (3) documents of states and successively smaller American governmental subdivisions (counties and cities, Chapter 13), and (4) bulletins of other countries (Chapter 14).

Books (Chapter 15) represent presumably the most permanent form of geologic publication. The next three chapters deal with miscellaneous and generally less important kinds of literature—newspapers (Chapter 16), theses (Chapter 17), and unpublished manuscripts (Chapter 18), the last two being closely related in that few theses are published. The book concludes with Chapter 19 on maps, which are an integral part of geologic literature even though not always thought of as such.

This arrangement is not based primarily upon a distinction between original and secondary sources, which is used as the chief basis of classification in some other guides to scientific literature. The real value of a publication lies in its recency, amount of detail, authoritativeness, selection of references, outlook, and general appropriateness under the circumstances. Thus an encyclopedia or textbook, although extreme examples of "secondary" sources of geologic literature, may be more useful in beginning a search than an "original" paper in a periodical.

This book had its origin in the author's long interest in bibliographic methods. It is the direct outgrowth of a collection of notes begun during the summer of 1944 in the Bibliographical Center for Research, Rocky Mountain Region, at the Denver Public Library, in an effort to accumulate at leisure the information that would eventually make it possible to secure a nearly complete list of references in the branch of geology that is his own specialty. Subsequent work has been done in the libraries of Harvard University, Colorado School of Mines, University of Colorado, and Colorado College.

The author's gratitude for ideas and data is due to the authors of similar books in other subjects, especially to the authors of the three chemistry books already referred to; to the directors, librarians, and secretaries of numerous institutions and public agencies who generously answered questions and sent published lists and other information; and to the faithful compilers of bibliographic material. Specific acknowledgments are made at appropriate places in the book. Personal thanks for valuable assistance go to Louise F. Kampf, Laura E. Tait, Grace G. Berger, and Helen Waring of the Coburn Library at Colorado College; Eulalia Chapman of the Bibliographical Center for Research, Rocky Mountain Region; Clara Cutright, Elizabeth Kingston, and Margaret Simonds of the Science and Engineering Department of the Denver Public Library; Virginia Holbert of the Geology Library of the University of Colorado; Edward A. Finlayson and A. B. Evans of the Library of Congress; Liberata Emmerich of the Pennsylvania State College Library; Ralph H. Phelps of the Engineering Societies Library; W. E. Rice of the U.S. Bureau of Mines; Rebecca B. Rankin of the New York Municipal Reference Library; and W. A. Bell of the Geological Survey of Canada. Dr. Howard A. Meyerhoff, Administrative Secretary of the American Association for the Advancement of Science, acted as adviser to the publishers, and his experienced counsel has been indispensable. The author's wife, Mignon, has also been of considerable help.

Corrections and suggestions for changes or additions in later printings of this book are earnestly solicited and will be gratefully received and acknowledged.

RICHARD M. PEARL

COLORADO SPRINGS, COLO.
January, 1951

CONTENTS

PART I

INTRODUCTION

CHAPTER 1

THE PROBLEM OF GEOLOGIC LITERATURE

As stated in the Preface, the abundance of scientific literature makes a guide such as this necessary in every field. In his use of the literature the geologist is faced with problems that are in certain ways unlike those of his colleagues in other sciences and of students of other subjects.

Some librarians regard the literature of mathematics as the most difficult to locate,[1] and the literature of chemistry is certainly many times more voluminous than that of geology. Furthermore, geologists are largely spared the concern of chemists and physicists with patents and patent literature.[2] Nevertheless, access to geologic literature is rendered difficult by the varied forms and complexity of sources in which the material appears. So great a proportion of the important writings in geology is contained in unbound or paper-bound booklets, pamphlets, and bulletins issued by widely scattered public agencies and so relatively little is found in regular periodicals and bound volumes that accumulating, classifying, labeling, storing, and making the literature available are a considerable and difficult task. In addition to ordinary printed publications (whatever the manner of presentation), numerous kinds of maps (with or without descriptive text) are an integral part of the literature of geology and must often be used in direct conjunction with the other materials, so that they can scarcely be filed apart without a serious loss in efficiency while they are in use.

For these reasons university libraries generally maintain separate geology libraries, usually in the building where geology classes are held, even though all their other departmental libraries may be kept in a central or main library building. There are very few exceptions to this rule among the leading American institutions of higher learning. Law libraries, because of their restricted nature, are perhaps the only other kind of library frequently handled similarly, but even they are less of a problem inasmuch as most law works are in bound volumes and are therefore easier to store, label, and circulate. In practically all instances, a law book is a law book,

---

[1] "Guide to the Literature of Mathematics and Physics" by Nathan Grier Parke III (McGraw-Hill Book Company, Inc., New York, 1947) is a useful guide to books (mostly) on mathematics.

[2] Discussions of patent literature that will be of value to geologic and mining engineers appear in the following books: Soule, Byron A., "Library Guide for the Chemist," McGraw-Hill Book Company, Inc., New York, 1938. Mellon, Melvin G., "Chemical Publications," 2d ed., McGraw-Hill Book Company, Inc., New York, 1940. Crane, E. J., and Austin M. Patterson, "A Guide to the Literature of Chemistry," John Wiley & Sons, Inc., New York, 1927.

and there is no difficulty in determining it to be one. ⌈Geology, on the other hand, is a composite of many sciences. It is directly dependent for its facts upon the contributions of each of the fundamental natural sciences —chemistry, physics, and biology—and their branches. Much of the content of geology consists of a specialized phase of one of these basic disciplines, and the rest is seriously indebted to them. ⌋

The "fields of work" classified by the School of Mineral Industries of the Pennsylvania State College indicate the subjects which proceed naturally from geology and its technologic aspects. Under the heading of Geo-technology are included the following divisions and subdivisions.

Earth sciences: Geology, Mineralogy, Geography, Geochemistry, Geophysics, Meteorology.
Mineral engineering: Mineral economics, Mining, Mineral preparation, Petroleum and natural gas.
Mineral technology: Fuel technology, Metallurgy, Ceramics.

Technology is emphasized in the following organizational structure of the American Institute of Mining and Metallurgical Engineers.[1]

Mining Branch
    Mining, Geology, and Geophysics Division
    Minerals Beneficiation Division
    Coal Division
    Industrial Minerals (Nonmetallics) Division
Metals Branch
    Institute of Metals Division
    Iron and Steel Division
    Extractive Metallurgy Division
Petroleum Branch
    Petroleum Division
No branch affiliation
    Mineral Economics Division
    Mineral Industry Education Division

The statistical study of P. K. L. Gross and A. O. Woodward[2] showed that geology was not at all well served by any single serial publication. This is in marked contrast to chemistry and physics, for which the *Journal of the American Chemical Society* and, to a lesser extent, the *Physical Review* because of their size and scope were virtually adequate as the sole source periodicals in their fields.

The literature of geology is, of course, international—far too much so for

[1] Robie, Edward H., Secretary, American Institute of Mining and Metallurgical Engineers, personal communication, Jan. 28, 1950.

[2] Gross, P. K. L., and A. O. Woodward, Serial Literature Used by American Geologists, *Science*, Vol. 73, pp. 660–664, 1931.

the peace of mind of the geologist who wants information without struggling for it. The late Lord Rayleigh once wrote: "By a fiction as remarkable as any to be found in law, what has once been published, even though it be in the Russian language, is usually spoken of as 'known.' " Such a slighting reference to the Russian language is no longer so appropriate as it used to be, not only because of the greatly increased amount of research coming from the Soviet Union, as an examination of the abstract journals will prove, but also because of the intensified nationalism which has resulted in the publication of papers in Russian that would previously have appeared in German, French, or English. Even if such material may not be available anywhere except as abstracts, we can no longer afford to leave it in obscurity, fervently though non-Russian readers might prefer to consign it to oblivion. (A discussion of translations appears in Chap. 6.)

The present strong trend toward more scientific and technical books is a major development in the history of publishing. Scientific and technical subjects are leading all others in demand in the Information Library program of the U.S. State Department. A respectable share of the vast funds being appropriated for research in almost all countries of the world is being applied to securing such literature; for example, plans for large-scale coordination of bibliographic material on research in Sweden were announced in 1947.[1]

The volume of geologic literature is increasing, but apparently at a slower rate than that of some other sciences. An actual decline in the amount of geologic literature has been shown in recent years, which the termination of the war has not yet been able to reverse. This may be due partly to the cessation of much geologic research (especially field work) during the war, while research continued or was expanded in other sciences. Even in books, however, there have been certain decreases in geologic publishing; for example, British technical book production from 1939 to 1946 showed many gains and some losses, geology showing the second largest decline among the 14 subjects recorded by *Whitaker's Cumulative Book Lists*.[2] But the over-all trend is undoubtedly upward, as indicated by the figures for 1947 and 1948.

Geologic literature—conveniently for the geologist, unfortunately for the science—stays current longer than much other scientific literature. Teachers of geology are wont to speak of a "recent discovery" or of something that was learned "not long ago" when they mean 10 or 20 years; to a physicist or chemist these were virtually prehistoric events. This hysteresis may in part be due to the long span over which the geologist reckons time,

[1] Thompson, James S., Technical Book Publishing in Europe, 1947, *Science*, Vol. 107, p. 47, 1947.
[2] *Ibid.*, p. 48.

but it is as much due to the plodding progress of the science, even in its technologic aspects.

A difficulty confronting the geologist in his search of the literature is the paucity of material available outside certain well-situated centers of learning, where almost every conceivable subject is adequately represented. Of the total of 552 depository libraries designated by the Congress as of June 1947 to receive government publications printed in Washington, only about half (including 125 libraries which get all Federal documents) elected to be "geological depositories" and receive the publications of the U.S. Geological Survey, although there is no charge for either the publications or postage and the only responsibility is that of housing them and making them available to inquirers. Certain other subject classifications, on the contrary, are requested by practically all the depository libraries. (For further information on depository libraries see pages 109 to 110.)

A given geologic publication, therefore, is much less likely to be available in the average library than a publication of no greater relative significance on, say, agricultural economics or public welfare statistics. This inadequacy of library facilities is being offset to a large extent by the growth of exchange facilities (discussed in Chap. 6) and photoprinting and microfilming services (also discussed in Chap. 6).

CHAPTER 2

CONDUCTING THE SEARCH

The method to be used in searching the literature of geology depends upon several factors. No one method can be suitable for all occasions.

Accessibility of the literature is less important now than it was formerly, owing to the extension of library facilities for lending, photoprinting, microfilming, and translating (each described in Chap. 6 of this book), but it does enter somewhat into consideration, if only because of the time and cost involved, moderate though they may be.

The personal ability and habits of the reader are major factors in the selection of methods for conducting the search. How much the reader already knows is always significant. Foreign literature, for example, is of value only as far as one is able to read the language, unless translations are secured. Furthermore, there is inevitably the person who conducts a literature search in the easiest and least appropriate fashion, like the man who, having lost a coin in the middle of the block, was seen looking for it under the corner street lamp because the light was better there.

The more familiar the reader is, even in a general way, with a wide range of literature and the various types of literature the more quickly he can decide which will best serve his purpose, just as a person with the most extensive general reading background can usually find most readily the best source for a particular bit of information when wanted.

The most essential factor in the choice of methods for searching the literature is the purpose underlying the investigation. Whether the search is conducted by a student, a writer of popular material, a compiler of a bibliography, a research worker, or a geologic engineer makes important differences. Looking up a standard fact in a handbook, table of constants, or other reference book requires a very different approach from that utilized in an exhaustive investigation of a general subject involving a compilation of all published material on that subject. The kinds of geologic literature discussed in the separate chapters of Part III are arranged in the general order that appears most suitable for the thorough investigation of a new problem. A different order, even a reverse order, might be more appropriate at certain times.

It is difficult to specify the order in which the literature should be examined because problems vary widely and several similar publications may have a different value in any given instance for a particular purpose. Formulating the specific question or problem is the first effort that is required. Such a formulation is best accompanied by setting up the desired

7

limitations, for without some arbitrary bounds there is little possibility of ever completely surveying a subject. Probably no subject exists in the real world with naturally defined limits; every subject grades imperceptibly in all directions into every other subject, including subjects not yet named or even recognized as existing. Stating and classifying the problem and securing the detailed information accompany each other; they will also overlap, for an examination of the references usually turns up new subjects. Subjects should be chosen beginning with the most specific, working toward those which are more and more general.

For other than an attempt at a completely exhaustive search, the desired orientation or bibliography may often be secured by studying an authoritative article in a good encyclopedia and examining the references recommended at the end or by studying a monograph, treatise, or textbook. The references given in these publications usually constitute a nucleus of the best material, especially that of a classical nature. Individual footnotes alone, however, may often refer merely to miscellaneous items or to published material less comprehensive than that desired for a starting survey. Such a general survey for purposes of orientation may be called "literature reconnaissance," the latter word being suggested by Parke.[1] Reconnaissance is a word especially familiar to geologists, even though the field work done under that name varies widely in scope and quality.

A starting point and an orientation similar to that furnished by articles in an encyclopedia can be secured through good reviews. These may be critical, or they may be in the nature of a summary, and they usually embrace a definite period of time. They may combine the features of historical survey, abstracts of recent developments, interpretation, forecast, and bibliography. The *Annual Reports on the Progress of Chemistry* issued by the Chemical Society (London) and described on page 169 have been among the most useful of such reviews in three branches of geology—Crystallography, Geochemistry, and Mineralogical chemistry. The subjects of geophysics, geomorphology, regional geology, and surveying are capably reviewed in *Geographisches Jahrbuch*, described on page 170. Other important annual geologic reviews include the "Review of Exploration and Developments" in the *Bulletin of the American Association of Petroleum Geologists*, the "Review of Petroleum Geology" in the *Colorado School of Mines Quarterly*, the *Annual Reviews of Petroleum Geology* published by the Institute of Petroleum, London, and the annual review numbers of *Mines Magazine, Mining Engineering, Journal of Metals*, and *Journal of Petroleum Technology*. The last publication continues the numbers of

[1] Parke, Nathan Grier, III, "Guide to the Literature of Mathematics and Physics," p. 8, McGraw-Hill Book Company, Inc., New York, 1947.

"Petroleum Development and Technology" that formerly appeared in *Transactions of the American Institute of Mining and Metallurgical Engineers.*

Addresses delivered at the annual meetings of geologic societies are often valuable reviews of the present state of the various sciences; these are usually printed in the official journal of the society or in general scientific periodicals such as *Science* and *Nature*. Symposiums published in periodicals, bulletins, or books are sometimes of especial value. Covering a longer period of time and mostly broader in viewpoint than the annual reviews are the splendid group of reviews on the progress in 21 fields of geology from 1888 to 1938 that were published in 1941 by the Geological Society of America, New York, in its fiftieth anniversary volume, "Geology, 1888–1938." A similar book, dealing with 12 aspects of the mineral industries, is "Seventy-five Years of Progress in the Mineral Industry, 1871–1946," edited by A. B. Parsons and published in 1948 by the American Institute of Mining and Metallurgical Engineers, New York, on the occasion of its seventy-fifth anniversary.

The most thorough kind of search, compiling and investigating every reference, begins with the indexes and bibliographies discussed in Chap. 7. These are chiefly lists of references on given subjects or by given authors. A useful technique is to compile a list of headings as one proceeds through the indexes, so that all likely authors, subjects, and words are kept prominently in view. Bibliographies may be annotated, taking on something of the nature of abstracts. Author indexes should be examined when a certain geologist is known to be an authority or frequent writer on the subject being studied. All references should be noted, even though they may prove upon closer examination to be irrelevant, inadequate, or otherwise inappropriate. The ones that are later retained should be copied in full, giving author, title, and place either on convenient index cards or on separate sheets of notebook paper, preferably loose-leaf.

Abstracts should then be examined in the abstract section of periodicals devoted to the subject being investigated and in the regular abstract journals, both of which are discussed in Chap. 8. The annotations will often serve to eliminate from further consideration many of the entries that were taken from the indexes and bibliographies. As much information as possible about the contents should be copied onto the index cards or notebook paper previously prepared in order to avoid making necessary any future reference to the original material, although it is quite inconvenient to do this in every case. Photoprints and microfilms, when available, are a preferred substitute for extensive copying.

The contents of an abstract should not be relied upon too fully. Important details may be omitted that are more essential to the reader than the parts of the original paper that have been quoted in the abstract. Also, the abstractor may have misinterpreted the viewpoint of the writer—infrequently, however, if he expects to continue his activities in that line. Reference to the original literature is advisable in such instances. If a useful article is abstracted in several different places, it is well worth while to read all the available abstracts; each may contain data or opinions not given in the others.

As far as up-to-date knowledge and inspiration for research are concerned, there is no adequate substitute for keeping up with current publications, especially in one's own specialized field in geology but only a little less so in other fields of geology and in other sciences. How the active person is going to be able to do this, considering the stupendous quantity of the current literature, has never been publicly explained. The abstract publications are the best aid in the attempt. Abstracts are not always of the most recent date, however; those abstract journals which strive for a comprehensive coverage of the literature will add items previously overlooked even though they may be more than a few years old. Included in this category will be foreign publications not previously available because of the war. Articles normally delayed in publication may also be older than "current literature" is usually deemed to be, even if the date of publication is very recent; the date of actual receipt by the editor is appended to many published papers.

Inasmuch as most abstracts pertain to material in periodicals, these should next be consulted (Chap. 9). Besides those containing the references specifically sought, the most important periodicals specializing in the subject being studied should be carefully searched. The tables of contents should be read, and the indexes scanned; annual, semiannual, and quarterly periodicals are especially convenient for this kind of survey. Duplicate reading of articles that appear in several places can be avoided by checking or filing separately the references that have been examined in an original source of publication, such as a periodical, as contrasted to those cursorily encountered in a secondary source, such as an abstract journal. Knowing the date or period at which the material was published is often a useful bit of knowledge, confining the search to limited volumes of periodicals.

When reference to an original article that is not at hand seems advisable because of one's having read an abstract of it, because it has been referred to favorably in other literature, because its title seems suggestive of a useful content, or because the author is known in that field, the paper may be made available in a number of ways. The periodical containing it can be borrowed from a library; this may be best when the paper is unusually lengthy, but it involves prompt return, postage or other shipping charges in both directions, and perhaps a rental fee. (Securing literature from libraries is discussed in Chap. 6.) Photoprints or microfilms, as discussed in Chap. 6, may be initially more expensive, but they can be kept and filed, and they save the long labor of copying from borrowed literature. If obtainable, reprints, preprints, offprints, or separates secured from authors or publishers by request, exchange, or purchase combine the useful features of both the original publication and a photoprint or microfilm reproduction. The original periodical can sometimes be purchased from the publisher, whether a firm, organization, or institution, or from dealers in used scientific periodicals. Frequently, owing to the limitations of space placed upon articles accepted for publication in periodicals, the original material has been so abbreviated that it may be wise to consult the author, who may be able and willing to make available the contents of his original paper.

Limiting dates are usually set arbitrarily for searching in the periodical literature. The date is a factor in the degree of comprehensiveness desired in searching. Recommendations have been made for setting the limits at 10 or 20 years prior to the date of making the search, in the belief that all prior material of any value has by then been incorporated into the more permanent literature of the various types of books discussed in Chap. 15. Such a time limit is much more likely to be suitable for a rapidly changing science such as physics or chemistry than for the less "progressive" science of geology Even so, it is hazardous to limit arbitrarily the dates of one's search in any field. Although much of the older work has been superseded by more thorough studies of later date, perhaps with new methods or equipment, and although much older work that is not obsolete has been incorporated into book form, a large amount of older periodical material is still useful. This is much more true in geology than in physics or chemistry because of the descriptive and regional character of much geologic research.

Books, likewise, need not be entirely useless merely because they are of an older date. In the transferring of data from periodical literature to books some details are omitted that may later prove to be those most necessary. Furthermore, material of a historical nature is never replaced, and the historical setting of research is a desirable background for almost every problem, furnishing perspective, inspiration, and a familiarity with the reasoning and method of approach of the leading geologists of former times. The nature of certain material, however, often makes desirable the use of a time limit. Information of scientific, not merely historical, value on geophysical prospecting, for example, could scarcely be expected prior to about 1919. The chief investigations on blowpipe methods in mineralogy were done in the nineteenth century, but practically all such information of value can be found in the standard textbooks.

The contents of bulletins are likely to be intermediate in scope and

permanency between those of periodicals and those of books. Some bulletins are indeed books according to many definitions of the term. Except
for the type of publisher, no significant differences exist among the various
kinds of bulletins discussed in Chaps. 10 to 14. It seems reasonable
enough to expect that the regional geology of a particular place is more
likely to appear in a publication issued by institutions and organizations
located in that area than in similar publications of distant localities.

The use of newspapers (Chap. 16) is confined to current items of scientific
interest, especially regarding personalities or technological developments;
an occasional historical item may also be gleaned from newspapers.

Although most theses (Chap. 17) are unpublished, they have been completed and "issued," at least in some easily read and reproducible manner,
and so they are reasonably conveniently available for consultation, either
direct or through the use of photoprints or microfilms.

Maps are a more or less independent adjunct to the other kinds of geologic
literature and deserve the separate treatment given them in Chap. 19.

In making a comprehensive search and often a less thorough search,
some persons work forward from the date at which they wish to start
whereas others begin with the most current material and work backward.
It is largely a matter of personal habit. Working backward has some
advantage in that references and footnotes repeatedly refer to prior material
of importance, which will then be recognized and given additional emphasis
when it is finally reached.

The law of diminishing returns serves to limit any exhaustive search.
When the time finally comes that further search does not yield reasonable
returns of useful new material, the sensible reader will probably stop.

The subject of the technique of reading accurately and rapidly— to best
advantage, in other words—is outside the scope of this book, but the
ability to appraise the reliability and experience of the author and the
recency of his material is an important asset to the reader, who must
share the responsibility with the editor of the periodical and the publisher
of the bulletin or book, although the committee that approves the academic
thesis ought to stand responsible for it.

Failure to find the material when first looked for is not necessarily a
complete barrier to locating it elsewhere. Original papers in foreign languages may be translated before being abstracted. A piece of literature
may be published in several different places, one of which may be more
accessible than the others. Some material may be included in another
work, perhaps in a more condensed yet still adequate form.

It is not amiss to emphasize the superiority of doing one's searching one-
self over having it done by someone less familiar with the subject, the problem, or the manner of investigation. The ultimate, if not the immediate,

value of alert but unhurried browsing through all kinds of literature has been expressed by experienced research workers in every field of knowledge.

The technique of preparing a bibliography, which, whether formally or informally, must accompany any report on a search of the literature, including recording the information and arranging the results, has not been dealt with here.   References on this subject will be found in periodicals and books under the entry Bibliography or Bibliographies.   Other library guides like this one; publications on the writing of scientific and technical books, articles, and theses; and the style manuals of the scientific and technical book publishing companies are the best places to find such information.

PART II

LIBRARY FACILITIES

CHAPTER 3

ARRANGEMENT OF THE LIBRARY

To facilitate the finding of publications in a library, a systematic arrangement is necessary. Several possible schemes may be employed. The most frequent are by (1) subject, (2) author, (3) title, (4) publisher, or (5) kind of publication. In practice, two or more of these methods are generally combined; for example, books may be arranged by subject (1), then grouped alphabetically by author (2) for each subject, all books (5) being kept separate from periodicals.

Geologic publications are often stored in a science and technology or similarly labeled room or department in a library, or in a special geology library in a large institution; such a segregation emphasizes on a large scale the subject matter.

An alphabetic arrangement of books by author is more common in geologic literature than in almost any other large subject. Geologists seem to be better known by name among their colleagues and even among students than are scientists in most other fields. This is partly owing to the deductive nature of geology and the personal aspects of geologic work. Such an arrangement by author is, however, more suitable for a library used largely by advanced students and professional geologists—and hence it is more likely to be found there—than it is for a library used mostly by the general public.

Titles are seldom used as a basis of classification, except that alphabetized titles may serve to subdivide works on a single subject; nevertheless, an arrangement by author is almost always preferred when numerous items are present on the same subject.

The better private publishers have endeavored for years to make their business names mean something to the reader, but it is still doubtful whether anyone but teachers, authors, and booksellers pay much attention to publishers' imprints, as publishers' trade names and trade-marks are called.

Arranging literature according to publisher is therefore mostly a matter of arranging it according to kind, inasmuch as the name of the publisher is of significance only when the publisher is an organization, such as a research foundation or an educational institution, or is a political entity; these publications are referred to as bulletins or public documents and are discussed in Chaps. 10 to 14.

Because most users of nonfiction material in libraries are far more interested in the subject than in the author, title, or publisher, the almost universal method of book classification is according to subject. Several different systems are in common use in the United States, and each is employed by libraries elsewhere.

The best known and most widely used system is the Dewey decimal classification, devised by Melvil Dewey at Amherst College in 1873. It is called a decimal system because the literature of all subjects is divided and subdivided by means of Arabic numerals decimally arranged. It is capable of indefinite expansion by the addition of extra figures. Ten "classes" are divided into 100 "divisions" and 1,000 "sections"; by adding a decimal point for ease in reading, each section in turn can be divided into 10 "subsections," and so on, into successively more detailed groups of 10 numbers. The numerical tables are supplemented by an alphabetic index of topics, known as a "relative index," giving the decimal number (and hence the exact location) of each entry and many synonyms and implied headings.

The Dewey classification is published by the Forest Press, Inc., Lake Placid Club, New York. In 1937 the Lake Placid Club Education Foundation established a joint committee of foundation trustees and American Library Association representatives to regulate editorial policies. The editorial work of the committee is carried on in the Decimal Classification Editorial Office, Library of Congress, Washington, D.C. Several editions are available, ranging from the "Decimal Classification and Relative Index," with tens of thousands of entries, to free lists of the 100 divisions. Dewey numbers of chief interest to geologists are included in the following list of sections:

No. 548. Crystallography
No. 549. Mineralogy
No. 550. Geology
  No. 551. Physical and dynamic geology
  No. 552. Lithology, Petrography, Petrology
  No. 553. Economic geology
  No. 554. Geology of Europe
  No. 555. Geology of Asia
  No. 556. Geology of Africa
  No. 557. Geology of North America
  No. 558. Geology of South America
  No. 559. Geology of Oceania, polar regions
No. 560. Paleontology
  No. 561. Plants
  No. 562. Invertebrates
    No. 563. Protozoans, Radiates
    No. 564. Mollusks
    No. 565. Articulates

No. 566. Vertebrates
    No. 567. Fishes, Batrachia
    No. 568. Reptiles, Birds
    No. 569. Mammals
No. 622. Mining engineering

The Brussels classification, or Universal decimal classification, is that of the Institut international de bibliographie, located in Brussels, Belgium. It is based on the Dewey classification but is carried one or more decimal places further, giving an enormous number of additional subdivisions. It is used direct in the *Manuel du répertoire bibliographique universel* and has been employed for scientific papers by several European periodicals (*Physics Abstracts, Chemisch Weekblad, Recueil des travaux chimiques des Pays-Bas,* etc.). The classification is contained in four volumes prepared by the Institut international de bibliographie and the Nederlandsch Instituut von Documentatie and published during 1927 to 1934 under the title "Classification decimale universelle." A fourth International Edition is in process of publication as B.S. 1,000 by the British Standards Institution. The Engineering Societies Library, New York (see page 27), is classified by this system. That part of the classification which pertains to mineralogy (548 and 549), taken from the complete German edition, is printed on pages 73 to 102 of *Fortschritte der Mineralogie, Kristallographie und Petrographie,* Vol. 25, 1935.

The Library of Congress uses its own system of classification, which has been adopted by other libraries. It is prepared by the Subject Cataloging Division of the Library of Congress; the classification, called "schedules," is sold by the Card Division of the Library of Congress, from which a price list of schedules still in print may be obtained free upon request. The first symbol in the code is a letter representing the major divisions called "classes," of which there are 20. The second symbol is another letter representing the "divisions" of each class. Numbers (one to four digits) are then used for further subdivision. The classes of chief interest to geologists are class *G*, Geography (including Anthropology and Folklore, etc.); class *Q*, Science; and class *T*, Technology. Each schedule has its own index with the Library of Congress symbol noted.

A greatly condensed outline of this classification, called "Outline of the Library of Congress Classification," may be secured free upon request from the Publications Office of the Library of Congress, Washington. The complete list of cross references is given in "Subject Headings Used in the Dictionary Catalogs of the Library of Congress," edited by Nella Jane Martin and published by the Subject Cataloging Division of the Library of Congress (5th ed., 1948, 1204 pp., obtainable from the Superintendent

of Documents, Government Printing Office, Washington). The Library
of Congress classification number is given for each separate subject heading. Cumulative supplements are published monthly; the latest supplements cover the periods from July 1947 to December 1949, and January to
June 1950.

Library of Congress classifications of chief interest to geologists are given
below:

G. Geography (general)
    1001–3035. Atlases
GA. Mathematical and astronomical geography
    101–1999. Cartography: map drawing, maps, works about maps. The maps
       themselves form a separate class in the custody of the Map Divison
GB. Physical geography
    401–638. Geomorphology: shore lines, reefs, islands, mountains, deserts, etc.
    651–2397. Water. Hydrology and hydrography: springs, rivers, waterfalls,
       lakes, ponds, etc.
GC. Oceanology and oceanography
    201–399. Dynamics of the sea: waves, currents, tides, deposits
QB. Astronomy
    275–341. Geodesy
QC. Physics
    811–849. Terrestrial magnetism
    851–999. Meteorology: temperature, rain, wind, weather, etc.
QD. Chemistry
    901–999. Crystallography
QE. Geology
    351–499. Mineralogy and petrology
    701–996. Paleontology. Paleozoology. Paleobotany
TN. Mineral industries: mining and metallurgy

The Cutter Expansive System, like the Library of Congress system, uses
letters for its main classes, including L for sciences and arts and R for
technology. This system was devised by Charles A. Cutter and edited and
enlarged by W. P. Cutter. Although it is scholarly, it is incomplete and
now out of date and hence little used. It evolved into the Library of
Congress system, which, however, incorporated features of other systems.

Additional schemes of classification are in use. Perhaps the most
comprehensive and profound is "A Bibliographic Classification" by Henry
E. Bliss, published by the H. W. Wilson Company, New York (Vol. 1,
1940; Vol. 2, 1947).

Certain libraries besides the Library of Congress use their own classification. That of the New York Public Library was devised by its former
director, John S. Billings, and is known as the Billings classification.

According to G. William Bergquist,[1] Chief of the Preparation Division, it is entirely suitable inasmuch as the library is a closed-shelf library in which the reader has no access to the shelves.

Books on the same subject are further classified alphabetically according to the surname of the author. Codes for these names are known as book numbers, book marks, author numbers, or Cutter numbers, and serve to distinguish any book from all others having the same class, subject, or shelf number. These numbers begin with the initial of the author's surname and are followed by two or three digits obtained from the following books: "Two-figure Alphabetic Order Table" by Charles A. Cutter, Library Bureau, 1906; "Three-figure Alphabetic Order Table" by Charles A Cutter, 2 vols., Library Bureau, 1902; or "Alphabetic Order Table Altered and Fitted with Three Figures" by Charles A. Cutter and Kate E. Sanborn, Library Bureau, 1896, or from adaptations of these lists for purposes of convenience.

Books by the same author are arranged by volume number (if there is more than one volume) and perhaps by date, the most recent ones being at the right. A chronological arrangement is used mostly in science, when the latest book is especially desired; Biscoe time numbers[2] are sometimes substituted for the actual date.

The combined class number (according to one of the above-mentioned systems of classification) and the Cutter number constitute the "call number" of a book. This differs from the "accession number," which is of little use except for inventory purposes, being merely a number indicating the order in which the book was added to the library.

The likelihood of books larger than the usual size being kept together on other shelves should be considered when a desired book seems to be absent. Many libraries mark with a dummy book the place where such an oversize book properly belongs. Valuable books may be kept in closed cabinets. Certain reference books may be kept in the library offices.

The other kinds of geologic literature besides books are usually arranged in separate groups. The system varies with the individual library.

Index publications (Chap. 7) and abstract journals (Chap. 8) may be placed with periodicals, with books, or on the reference shelves.

Periodicals (Chap. 9) are usually placed on the shelves alphabetically by name, but sometimes they may be given classification numbers corresponding to the subject field and placed in numerical order.

Bulletins issued by United States government agencies (Chap. 10), such

[1] Bergquist, G. William, Chief of the Preparation Division, New York Public Library, personal communication, Aug. 5, 1947.

[2] Biscoe, W. S. C., Chronological Arrangement of Books on Shelves, *Library Jour.*, Vol. 10, pp. 246–247, 1885.

as those of the Geological Survey, are generally classed as documents and arranged according to the agency.   Bulletins published by organizations and institutions (Chap. 11), such as the Carnegie Institution of Washington, are likely to be found alphabetically according to publisher.   Bulletins issued by the state geologic surveys (Chap. 12) are usually arranged alphabetically by states but kept apart from bulletins issued by other state agencies and organizations.   County bulletins and city bulletins (Chap. 13) of geologic interest will probably have to be looked up in the library card catalogues.   Bulletins of foreign countries (Chap. 14) are always kept separately; only the larger libraries of the United States have more than a few of them of geologic importance, except Canadian bulletins.

Newspapers (Chap. 16), theses (Chap. 17), and maps (Chap. 19) are grouped separately from these other kinds of literature and from one another, owing to their very different form.

Further information on classifying and cataloguing is found in publications of the American Library Association, Chicago; most of these books are available in libraries, and a catalogue may be had upon request from the Association.   Other books and articles are indexed in the general literature indexes, especially in the annotated *Library Literature*, published from 1936 to 1942 and since January 1946 by the H. W. Wilson Company, New York. Older similar indexes are *Bibliography of Library Economy*, published for 1876 to 1920 by the American Library Association, and *Library Literature*, published for 1921 to 1932 by the American Library Association and for 1933 to 1935 by the H. W. Wilson Company.

CHAPTER 4

LIBRARY CATALOGUES

The basic index, or directory, to the library is the systematic collection of cards known as a card catalogue. The cards may be grouped alphabetically in separate drawers in a library filing cabinet according to (1) author, (2) subject, or (3) title or (4) numerically by the Dewey decimal classification or one of the other similar systems discussed in Chap. 3. Rarely, arrangements by (5) publisher or (6) time of publication are employed for their specific usefulness.

The file of cards disposed according to the fourth method is known as a "classed catalogue" or more commonly as a "shelf list," because it is arranged in the order that the books are placed on the shelves. The cards pertaining to sets of books or periodicals are often followed by cards called "holdings cards" which are marked from time to time to indicate the volumes or parts of the set or series that are actually in the library. The cards for periodicals (including holdings cards) are usually grouped separately, although they may be included with book publications, or both methods may be used in the same library.

Catalogue cards have long been prepared by individual libraries, with consequent variations in style. Increased uniformity has been made possible by the printing and distribution of cards by the Library of Congress, the John Crerar Library, the H. W. Wilson Company, and a few other organizations.

The Library of Congress issues a catalogue card for each book granted a United States copyright, as well as for other published material, as opportunity permits. These cards are sold to libraries and individuals, and a service is maintained for the distribution of all cards printed on any desired subject during the preceding month.

The author is regarded as the chief member of the trio—author, printer, publisher—responsible for the publication of a book. Hence the "author entry" is the "main entry" on the Library of Congress catalogue cards; the "unit card" is the original author card issued by the Library of Congress. The unaltered Library of Congress unit card for a well-known geology book is reproduced in Fig. 1, page 24, as an example.

Author
   1. Full name of chief author or editor
   2. Date of birth, for identification purposes
   3. Date of death, for identification purposes

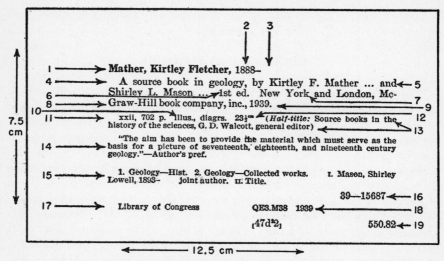

FIG. 1. Library of Congress unit card. (*Printed with permission of the Librarian of Congress.*)

Title
  4. Title of book as given in full on the title page
  5. Names of authors as given on the title page
  6. Edition
Imprint
  7. Place of publication
  8. Publisher
  9. Date of publication
Collation
  10. Photographs, drawings, maps, and other nontext material
  11. Number of pages
  12. Height of book
Notes
  13. Series
  14. Information about contents
  15. Additional headings for card indexing (subjects, authors, title)
  16. Number for ordering card
  17. Publisher of card
  18. Library of Congress classification
  19. Dewey decimal classification

Additional kinds of information appear on other such cards. Of value is the mention of bibliographies where they are an important feature of the book. Particularly important entries (not necessary on the above card) are the "analytics," which identify the parts or other major divisions of a book or set of books.

A more extended discussion of all the printed entries, notations, and symbols on Library of Congress catalogue cards, with detailed historical notes as to past practices, appears in Part 2 (pp. 6–12) of "Handbook of Card Distribution," which can be obtained from the Card Division, Library of Congress, Washington (7th ed., 1944, reprinted 1946, 88 pp.).

The call number (discussed on page 21) is usually typed by the local library on the unit card (the author card) above or next to the author entry, so that it can be seen quickly at the upper left edge of the card. Cards in the "shelf list" would be this kind of card arranged numerically according to call number.

Each subject according to which it is desired to index a book is usually typed in red or black at the top of a separate unit card. The call number is also added. These "subject cards" may range in number from one to half a dozen or more for each book if the scope of the book warrants. It is likely that each subject suggested on the Library of Congress unit card (see 15, Fig. 1) will be represented, and many more may be included if the library is a sufficiently specialized one. These additional subjects serve the same purpose as cross references in an index.

"Title cards" are not prepared so often as they used to be, because the title is prominently displayed below the author's name. However, when no author is indicated or when the title is especially distinctive or conveys useful information about the contents of a book (and sometimes when it does not), it may be typed in black in the upper left corner of the card. The call number is also added. Articles, prepositions, and other short, common, or nondistinctive words are ignored in listing titles, and the card is entered under the first significant word of the title —thus, "A *Source Book in Geology*." When a file of author cards is kept separately, periodicals, series, sets, and anonymous publications are entered by title in the card catalogue, though perhaps placed at the back.

Titles of periodicals and bulletins are entered under the name of the organization which published them if the name is considered by librarians to be part of the title. Otherwise, or if no organization is involved, the entry is made as though for a book, that is, under the first significant word of the title. Some periodicals are, for historical reasons, catalogued in what seems to be an obscure order because the name that is most familiar is not used as the entry. Twenty-five such scientific periodicals are listed by Soule,[1] who also suggests[2] that current periodicals difficult to locate should be looked up in the "List of Periodicals Abstracted" by *Chemical Abstracts*. The latest list is in Vol. 40, No. 24, Pt. 2, of *Chemical Abstracts*,

[1] Soule, Byron A., "Library Guide for the Chemist," p. 21, McGraw-Hill Book Company, Inc., New York, 1938.
[2] *Ibid.*, p. 17.

Dec. 20, 1946, 209 pp.   Other suggestions of this kind are given in this book in Chap. 5. on Indexing.

When these separate kinds of cards (except numerical classification cards) are combined in a single over-all alphabetical file of author cards, subject cards, and title cards, as is usually done, the collection is called a "dictionary card catalogue."   The guide cards inside the drawer and the codes on the outside aid in locating the desired information more quickly.

Although there are as many variations in card catalogues as there are libraries, it is nevertheless often useful for the reader to be acquainted with the rules that are more or less widely accepted as standard.   The general principles of cataloguing, the detailed rules, and the terms employed are discussed in the following manuals recommended for that purpose:

"Simple Library Cataloging" by Susan G. Akers, 3d ed., American Library Association, Chicago, 1944, 197 pp.

"Introduction to the Cataloging and the Classification of Books" by Margaret Mann, 2d ed., American Library Association, Chicago, 1943, 267 pp.

"Guide to the Cataloguing of Periodicals" by Mary Wilson McNair, 3d ed., Library of Congress, Washington, 1925 (reprinted 1938), 23 pp.

"Guide to the Cataloguing of the Serial Publications of Societies and Institutions" by Harriet W. Pierson, 2d ed., Library of Congress, Washington, 1931, 128 pp.

"Author Entry for Government Publications" by James B. Childs, Library of Congress, Washington, 1941, 38 pp.

"Handbook of Card Distribution," 7th ed., Library of Congress, Washington, 1944 (reprinted 1946), 88 pp.

"A.L.A. Cataloging Rules for Author and Title Entries" by Clara Beetle, 2d ed., American Library Association, Chicago, 1949, 265 pp.

"Rules for Descriptive Cataloging in the Library of Congress," Library of Congress, Washington, 1949, 141 pp.

"A.L.A. Rules for Filing Catalog Cards," American Library Association, Chicago, 1942, 109 pp.

"Rules for a Dictionary Catalog" by Charles A. Cutter, 4th ed., U.S. Bureau of Education, Washington, 1904, 173 pp.

Besides its appearance on the catalogue card itself, the order number by which a card may be purchased from the Library of Congress can be determined in numerous other ways which are listed on pages 38 to 40 of "Handbook of Card Distribution," published for free limited distribution by the Card Division, Library of Congress, Washington.

In the same "Handbook of Card Distribution," and in a greatly condensed mimeographed brochure titled "Library of Congress Printed Cards: How to Order and Use Them" will be found the necessary information for purchasing these cards.

The series publications of American and foreign geologic surveys and bureaus of mines for which separate analytical Library of Congress catalogue cards are available are listed in Part C of *Bulletins* 16 to 19 of the Catalog Division of the Library of Congress, 4th ed., 1932, and *First Supplement, 1932–1934; Special Supplement, 1935–1937;* and *Special Supplement Number 2, 1938–1939.*

The Library of Congress issues proof sheets of its catalogue cards, struck off before the cards are printed and available either on white paper or on a stiffer manila paper. Most proof sheets contain five titles. Each proof sheet has a heading showing to what class the books on it belong, so that proof sheets can be ordered on certain wanted subjects. Present classes of interest to geologists are Geography and anthropology, Maps and charts, Science, Technology, Titles from Library of Congress Map Division, Titles from Smithsonian Institution, and Titles from U.S. Geological Survey. The proof sheets are mailed daily, weekly, or monthly as desired. They can also be furnished in card size and punched.

The catalogue cards printed and sold by the John Crerar Library, Chicago, are author cards somewhat similar to those of the Library of Congress. Effort is made to exclude from the scope of the current stock titles for which Library of Congress cards are available.

Catalogue cards for author, title, and subject (including analytics) have been printed since 1938 by the H. W. Wilson Company, New York, but since they deal largely with popular books, only a few are on geologic subjects, and these are the less technical books or the more general ones, including some of the standard works, of which the following are examples: "Dana's System of Mineralogy" (Palache-Berman-Frondel), "Architecture of the Earth" (Daly), "Physiography of the Eastern United States" (Fenneman).

The Engineering Index Service, New York, issues annotated library-size (3 by 5 inches) catalogue cards of current world-wide technical, scientific, and industrial literature in 287 divisions. The subject of the division appears at the top of the card. These cards are mailed to subscribers daily (for all divisions) or weekly (for selected divisions) at annual rates which vary according to the subject covered. The cards are combined yearly into an annual volume called *The Engineering Index*, described on page 79. A description of the divisions and the prices are given in an indexed circular obtainable free upon request. Among the divisions of geologic interest are the following:

No. 11. Aluminum and other light-metal products
No. 17. Bituminous materials
No. 20. Brass, bronze, and copper
No. 33. Clay and clay products
No. 34. Coal and other solid fuels

No. 35. Coal mining
No. 78. Geology
No. 79. Geophysics
No. 92. Hydrology, meteorology, and seismography
No. 106. Lead, tin, zinc, and antimony products
No. 108. Lime and limestone
No. 122. Metal mining
No. 127. Mineralogy and rare metals and elements
No. 129. Mining engineering
No. 130. Mining geology
No. 136. Natural gas and gasoline
No. 140. Nonferrous metals
No. 141. Nonmetallic minerals
No. 143. Oil-field operation
No. 146. Ore treatment
No. 151. Petroleum engineering
No. 152. Petroleum geology
No. 153. Petroleum refining
No. 176. Refractory materials
No. 180. Rock products
No. 183. Salt and saline deposits
No. 184. Sand and gravel
No. 203. Surveying
No. 216. Water resources

Catalogue cards to periodical articles are a feature of *Acta Polytechnica*, a new periodical issued by the Royal Swedish Academy of Engineering Research and designed to publish in monograph form in four languages the results of outstanding current Swedish technical research. The weekly issues of *The British National Bibliography* (see page 180), in which almost all current British books, pamphlets, and government bulletins are catalogued according to the Dewey decimal classification, are printed on one side of the paper to facilitate clipping, mounting, and filing as cards. Annotated catalogue cards of current French and occasionally Belgian books are issued at irregular intervals by *Le Fichier bibliographique*, Paris.[1]

A few other institutions and organizations print catalogue cards for sale or distribution. A history of cooperative cataloguing up to the date of the establishment of the Library of Congress cards is given in "Co-operative Cataloging" by William Blease (*Library Journal*, Vol. 40, pp. 708–713, 1915) and in references listed in "Bibliography of Cooperative Cataloging and the Printing of Catalog Cards (1850–1902) " by Torstein Jahr and A. J. Strohm (*Report of the Librarian of Congress*, June 30, 1902; also reprinted separately, 1903).

[1] Worley, Parker, Current National Bibliographies, II, *Library of Cong. Quart. Jour. of Current Acquisitions*, Vol. 7, No. 1, p. 17, 1949.

Commercial card indexes maintained by commercial firms serving the petroleum industry in the United States include data pertaining to completion, production, paleontology, and correlation. These card catalogues and some that are kept by educational institutions and public agencies are described in Chap. 12 of "Subsurface Geologic Methods" by L. W. LeRoy and Harry M. Crain (Colorado School of Mines, Golden, Colorado, 1949).

Library catalogues are occasionally prepared in forms other than cards. In spite of the cost of printing and the fact that the catalogues are soon out of date, some of the leading libraries in the world have published book catalogues of their holdings, because they occupy less space than card files, are portable, and can be widely distributed. Printed catalogues of many geologic libraries are listed in columns 1155 to 1159 of "A World Bibliography of Bibliographies" by Theodore Besterman (2d ed., Pt. 1, privately published in London, 1947). Many European libraries use sheaf catalogues which consist of cards or slips held in a loose-leaf binder (a sort of combination of book and card catalogue), especially where the cards are not printed.

CHAPTER 5

INDEXING

To be really adequate an index must be better than the average one. The necessity for thorough indexing is usually obvious to those who have tried to secure as much information from a piece of published literature as they desired without actually reading it all. Knowledge that is hidden is of little value. As the user of a given publication continues to become better acquainted with its contents, he should also endeavor to become more familiar with the nature of its index, as well as with any outside indexes that may also exist to cover the same contents. Crane and Patterson considered the indexing of scientific literature important enough to warrant the second largest chapter in "A Guide to the Literature of Chemistry."[1]

No publication can be so minutely classified and arranged as to obviate the need for an index. Reference material is generally not much better than the available indexes. Even a dictionary has its index in the form of cross references, and the addition of an index surely does not impair the usefulness of an encyclopedia. Publishers of serious books are coming to appreciate the value of good indexes and are stressing the index as an integral part of the book, fully as important as anything else. Other types of literature require indexes even more than books and bulletins do. In extensive bibliographic publications the index is the better half, although short bibliographic lists can do without one. In abstract journals the index is at least a full partner to the abstracts. In periodicals the index is a useful adjunct to the table of contents and the articles themselves.

Indexing is an art (so is index using) that requires patience, precision, and a knowledge of the subject. Better indexes are prepared by professional index makers than by the average author, but an author who is familiar with the technique of index preparation can create the most useful index because he has the most thorough grasp of the contents and knows best what should be emphasized. Subject entries, not words as in a concordance, are the proper grist for the index.

The value of an index does not lie solely in its size; an occasional example of a too detailed index, far more confusing than helpful because of extreme repetition, has been published in certain volumes known to dealers in antiquarian books.

Errors can sometimes be corrected by locating the same reference under a

[1] Crane, E. J., and Austin M. Patterson, "A Guide to the Literature of Chemistry," John Wiley & Sons, Inc., New York, 1927.

different heading or by supplementing the search by using a different kind of index (such, for example, as an author or locality index instead of a subject index) if any other kind is available and the correlative information is known. For example, in a European book known to the author the mineral cryolite is wrongly indexed, but it can be found under its chemical class and two of its localities if the reader happens to know any of these three facts. Finding author entries to best advantage requires a knowledge of the many possible ways in which the name may be spelled or indexed, as discussed on pages 34 to 36. Transposition (as 219 instead of 291) is a common error in indexes.

The index to a library is the arrangement of the individual cards in the card catalogue. The general rules that apply to this arrangement, discussed in Chap. 4, are likewise applicable to the internal indexing of the publications themselves.

Indexes may be comprehensive or specific. In a comprehensive index subjects, authors, and titles are entered together as they are in a "dictionary card catalogue" (see page 26). When the same leading word is used for more than one kind of entry, it is usually customary to place author entries first, followed by title entries and then by subject entries. Numbers used in titles or as subjects are entered as though spelled out; thus 21 is entered as Twenty-one and would be followed alphabetically by Twenty-three and Twenty-two in that order. Titles are alphabetized under the first significant word, as discussed on page 25.

Specific indexes include entries of one kind only, as author or title indexes. The kinds that may be used depend upon the type and the scope of the publication. The most frequently used kinds are author and subject indexes; the latter may be headed "general index" where other indexes appear separately. Arrangement of these two important indexes will be discussed below. Formula indexes are common in chemical publications. Patent-number indexes are common in chemical, physics, and engineering or other technical publications, of which those dealing with mining are of chief interest to the geologist. (Patent literature, however, is not discussed in this book; see instead the references given in the footnote on page 3). Specialized subject indexes are often used in publications in special fields of geology.

Thus an index to mineral species is characteristic of publications on mineralogy. Different styles of type are often employed to distinguish between species and varieties. "A Textbook of Mineralogy," by Dana and Ford,[1] has also a few entries in a third style of type for mineral groups and

[1] Dana, Edward S., and William E. Ford, "A Textbook of Mineralogy," 4th ed., John Wiley & Sons, Inc., New York, 1932.

chemical classes.   Although "Dana's System of Mineralogy"[1] has only one index, it contains mineral names exclusively and so is this same kind of index; numbered and accepted species are printed in boldface type, whereas uncertain species, varieties, and obsolete names are printed in lower-case type.

Indexes to genera and species are prominent in publications on paleontology.   The index to genera in Shimer and Shrock's "Index Fossils of North America"[2] includes subgenera, families, orders, classes, and phyla; a separate index includes species only.

Because of the peculiar nature of geologic work, an index to localities may be featured in material on mineralogy, paleontology, or almost any other branch of geology.

The reader should always be aware that occasional confusing indexes exist which attempt to introduce some sort of classification.   The former "title" indexes to *Nature*, with separate groupings under Astronomical notes, Correspondence, Deaths, and classified Reviews, were not so objectionable as others of this kind, inasmuch as each of the items in these various groups was also entered in the proper place in the main title and name indexes.

A set of books may have a general index in addition to separate indexes to each volume.   Most periodicals are indexed annually, with the index sometimes bound at the beginning instead of the end.   When a periodical is bound into more than one volume, the index, if an annual one, is usually placed at the end of the last volume for the year.   Cumulative indexes, covering a longer period (usually 5 years or multiples), are available for certain periodicals.   These are valuable aids, facilitating a search that extends over a period of years.   The frequency of indexing and the existence of cumulative indexes are indicated in some of the lists of periodicals enumerated in Chap. 9.

Any explanatory material at the beginning of an index should be read, for time may well be saved in the long run.   Remarks as to cross references, the meaning of the various styles of type, and symbols or abbreviations should be noted.

The books on cataloguing that are listed in Chap. 4 will also be found useful for the study of indexing.

AUTHOR INDEXES

In discussing the indexing of authors' names, differentiation should be made between entries that pertain to the actual authors who have written

[1] Palache, Charles, Harry Berman, and Clifford Frondel, "Dana's System of Mineralogy," 7th ed., John Wiley & Sons, Inc., New York, 1944.

[2] Shimer, Henry W., and Robert R. Schrock, "Index Fossils of North America," John Wiley & Sons, Inc., New York, 1944.

the material or whose writings are being abstracted and entries that merely mention the names of persons, perhaps quoting their work or opinions. Name indexes are used only in books, where there can be no possible confusion with an author index, except in the remote case of a compilation of contributions from a number of authors. In an encyclopedia, as a somewhat different instance, the names of contributors are listed as such whereas the names of other persons fit into the subject index.

In addition to the actual writer, the "author" of a book may be an editor, compiler, translator, or corporate body, such as an institution, society, or association, or public agency.

The author entry on a library catalogue card is the true name of the person if known; when the pseudonym is widely familiar (perhaps more so than the real name), it will probably be found as a cross reference at the proper place in the alphabet. Pseudonyms, however, are rare in scientific literature. Geologists being what they are, anonymous contributions are even rarer.

Coauthors are known to indexers and librarians as "joint authors." When there are two or three authors of an article in a periodical, each is usually entered separately. When there are more authors, the entry is often made only under the first of the names, for example, M. H. Billings et al.[1] or and others.[2] All the joint authors of books are given separate entries unless one author is accepted as the editor; then the book is entered only under his name. Collaboration of more than two authors on an equal basis takes place mostly in the writing of textbooks. One of the best known texts in general geology[3] has three joint authors, and another[4] has four.

Company names occur only occasionally as author entries; the practice is common, however, in patent literature, where foreign firms (which are allowed to secure patents) may sometimes be listed in several European languages, perhaps with cross references to each entry. Company names are entered under the more significant words.

The spelling of names must be examined with greater care than that of ordinary words, because there is seldom any objective check for the copyist or proofreader as there is with dictionary words. A name may have almost any spelling, and frequently it does. Part of the trouble lies in trying to

---

[1] Billings, M. H., et al., Geophysical Prospecting, Am. Assoc. Petroleum Geologists Bull., Vol. 24, No. 2, pp. 372–373, 1940.

[2] Abstract of article mentioned in footnote 1 in Annotated Bibliography Econ. Geology, Vol. 13, No. 1, p. 117, 1941.

[3] Longwell, Chester R., Adolph Knopf, and Richard F. Flint, "A Textbook of Geology," 2d ed., John Wiley & Sons, Inc., New York, 1939.

[4] Emmons, William H., George A. Thiel, Clinton R. Stauffer, and Ira S. Allison, "Geology: Principles and Processes," 3d ed., McGraw-Hill Book Company, Inc., New York, 1949.

follow pronunciations. Rarely, a duplication or even a triplication may occur with the same name, owing to changes during copying.

The matter of spelling affects names chiefly in the following categories:

Umlaut. In 1936 the Mineralogical Society of America and the Mineralogical Society (Great Britain) agreed to add *e* after the vowel instead of placing an umlaut (as ä, ö, ü) above it, in accordance with the alternate choice among Germans.[1] *Chemical Abstracts* also puts the umlaut as *ae*, etc. A name containing an umlaut or its equivalent *e* may consequently be found in either alphabetical place in an index. The umlaut may also have been intended but have been omitted in typesetting, so its absence must occasionally be anticipated.

ø. The Norwegian and Danish letter *ø* may appear as it is and be indexed as *o*, or it may be replaced by an umlauted *ö* or "modernized" to *oe* as though it were German.

å. The Swedish letter *å* may appear that way, be reduced to *a*, or be replaced by *aa* or less often by *o* or *oa*.

CH. The Spanish *CH* is a separate letter and should be alphabetized after the *C*'s, but it may be indexed as though it were English.

Russian names. In *Chemical Abstracts* these are transliterated according to "Webster's New International Dictionary of the English Language" (2d ed., G. &. C. Merriam Company, Springfield, Mass., 1934). This is closely similar to the Library of Congress system and is the practice of the American Library Association (1941) and the Government Printing Office.

Japanese names. In *Chemical Abstracts* these are transliterated according to the Hepburn system.

Other non-Arabic names. These present special problems; the need for standardization is usually satisfied by following the rules used by the Library of Congress, the Government Printing Office, the Board on Geographic Names, or some similar authority. The basic references on the transliteration of all known languages are given on pages 79 to 80 of "Aids to Geographical Research" by John Kirtland Wright and Elizabeth T. Platt, 2d ed., American Geographical Society, New York, 1947.

Spelling is involved indirectly in the following instances of difficult location of names. Instead, the manner of indexing causes most of the trouble.

Mac. Names beginning with *M'*, *Mc*, and *Mac* are usually indexed as though written Mac—, whether or not the second part of the name begins with a capital letter. A few indexes irrationally place the names that stand with *M'* or *Mc* in a separate group, before or after the rest of *M*'s.

Saint. Names beginning with *St.* or *Ste.* are usually indexed as though they were unabbreviated, thus, *Saint, Sainte,* respectively.

[1] *Am. Mineralogist,* Vol. 9, pp. 60–65, 1924; Vol. 21, pp. 188–191, 1936.

Titles. Names of persons having titles are usually indexed under the titled name instead of the surname.

Married women. Women scientists who have married may have their names indexed under either their maiden or married name. When the entry pertains to an actual publication bearing the woman's name, it would, of course, be indexed the way it was printed. In an incidental reference it may appear either way.

Monsieur. A slight irregularity in the position of a French name in an index may be occasioned by the erstwhile common practice of some Frenchmen to sign their papers with their surname only (imitating Napoleon, perhaps), preceding which the editor or printer might place an *M* for Monsieur, although the given name may have actually begun with any letter from *A* to *Z*. If the true initials are sometimes determined and sometimes not, the same name or several similar names may be confused in various indexes.

Spanish names. Fortunately fewer than German or French names, these are complicated to index. They may be especially troublesome on account of the permissible use of both the paternal name and the maternal maiden name or the former alone. With the inversion possible in an index, the same name may be indexed in any one of the following ways.

Bermudez y Hernandez, Pedro Joaquin
Bermudez Hernandez, Pedro Joaquin
Bermudez H., Pedro Joaquin

Still other possibilities, more common in literary than scientific literature, are discussed in "Spanish Personal Names" by Charles F. Gosnell (the H. W. Wilson Company, New York, 1938, 112 pp.).

Compound names. These names may be indexed under either part, so that, for example, T. Hodge-Smith (whether printed with or without the hyphen) may appear as either Hodge-Smith, T., or Smith, T. Hodge, or perhaps as both with a cross reference to the one preferred.

Prefixes. Names that begin with prefixes cause uncertainty because they may be indexed several different ways. The entry may be made under the prefix (as de Witt, Wallace, Jr.) or under the main part of the name (as Sitter, L. U. de). In the former instance, the name, including the prefix, may be indexed as a unit, or the prefix alone may be considered first. Cross references help to simplify some of the various possibilities. The preference of the author is generally followed whenever it is known.

Group names. Names of organizations, institutions, and public agencies may be indexed in various ways which, in the absence of cross references, should be watched for. Examples are the following.

United States Geological Survey
Geological Survey, United States

Interior, Department of, Geological Survey
Department of Interior, Geological Survey

Besides the errors of spelling and indexing, confusion originates in tracing similar names (as Francis Shepard, George Shepherd, and Charles Shappard), vernacular names (as Bauer for Agricola), and duplicate names for the same person occasioned by the marriage of a woman (as Margaret Fuller Boos) or the elevation of a scientist to the ranks of the nobility. The reader should bear these possibilities in mind when making his search. Complications also arise in the indexing of editorials, anonymous contributions, and articles signed by initials (especially letters and reviews).

The books on cataloguing that are listed in Chap. 4 contain useful information on the rules for indexing authors' names.

SUBJECT INDEXES

As the capable writer of a good book is the person best qualified to prepare an index because he knows most about the contents, so the well-informed geologist is better able to make fuller use of an index than someone else, even a general librarian, who is less acquainted with the subject and its ramifications. A knowledge of indexing procedure is, however, necessary to do the job best. The best indexes, which utilize subjects rather than mere words, demand a wider knowledge on the part of the user than poorer indexes that are prepared mechanically. The proper entry may not be at all the same as the usage in the original publication, but it should be more appropriate; that is, it should be what the trained reader is most likely to look for. Even additional cross-reference entries, for less trained readers, may likewise not include the wording of the original publication. The words in titles may be superfluous when indexed, especially if the title is prepared with the looseness of a popular magazine article rather than the precision expected of a scientific article. An article, furthermore, may contain information of value on subjects not hinted at in the title.

Index entries may be listed according to (1) the alphabetical order of the first word taken by itself, this being the standard of alphabetizing used by the majority of American libraries, as

rock
rock salt
rocker

or (2) according to the several words of an entry taken as a unit (only those preceding the comma if the phrase is transposed), as is done in "Webster's New International Dictionary" and telephone directories, as

rock
rocker
rock salt

In the second method, compound words which can be joined to make a single word lead to confusion. The relationship between the main heading and its modifications varies, but usually a heading by itself precedes a heading with modifications. The reader should be alert to the various possibilities and look elsewhere in the vicinity of the entry he wants to find.

The user of indexes should learn to look up, besides the subject that he has in mind, the following:

1. All related subjects, as many as he can think of.
2. The main heading under which the subject falls, that is, the more general subject, such as the group name of a chemical compound.
3. The significant subdivisions which the subject covers, that is, the more specific entries, as Ilmenite for Titanium.
4. All reasonable synonyms, as Gems, Precious stones.
5. Important antonyms, as Stress, Strain.
6. The popular equivalent of a scientific term, as Earthquakes for Seismology.
7. The scientific equivalent of a popular term, as Fluviatile for Stream.
8. Other scientific equivalents of a term, as Ferrous, Ferric for Iron.
9. "See" and "see also" entries.
10. The names, in the author index, of scientists known to have worked on or written about the subject.
11. The names, in the locality index, of places associated with the subject.
12. Variations in word order, that is, inversions.

In actual practice, words that might be appropriate suggest themselves as the search continues. As stated before, other factors (such as patience and time) being equal, the reader with the widest background of learning will find the largest number of entries. The most extensive list of subject headings and cross references yet published is "Subject Headings Used in the Dictionary Catalogs of the Library of Congress," edited by Nella Jane Martin and published by the Subject Cataloging Division of the Library of Congress, Washington (5th ed., 1948, 1204 pp.). Cumulative supplements are published monthly. The Library of Congress classification number is given for each separate entry.

Proper names, other than those of the actual or legal authors, are used as subjects and are included in the subject indexes, except in the occasional book where they are indexed separately. Some publications that are chiefly of chemical interest have separate formula indexes. Crane and Patterson[1] discuss at length the problem of chemical compounds, both inorganic and organic. Mineral and fossil names are of prime interest to the geologist; these are referred to on pages 31 to 32 of this book.

The difficulties in indexing connected with the use of foreign-language

[1] Crane, E. J., and Austin M. Patterson, "A Guide to the Literature of Chemistry," pp. 176–188, John Wiley & Sons, Inc., New York, 1927.

publications, not the least of which is German compounding, are best re-solved by reference to an English–foreign-language dictionary. German indexing will probably place words with an umlaut in the same order as though the umlaut were not required at all.

The books on cataloguing that are listed in Chap. 4 contain useful information on the standard rules for subject indexing.

CHAPTER 6

LIBRARY SERVICES

The legion of services that libraries and librarians have long rendered to students, scholars, scientists, and the broader public is the true tribute to a vital institution and a noble profession. Any attempt to enumerate these services would be inadequate, and the frequent user of a library eventually finds them out for himself.

According to the report of the American Library Association Board on Resources in American Libraries,[1] the following libraries in the United States, arranged here alphabetically, contain the most important collections of geologic publications:

University of Alabama, University, Ala.
American Museum of Natural History, New York, N.Y.
University of California, Berkeley, Calif.
University of Chicago, Chicago, Ill.
Columbia University, New York, N.Y.
Cornell University, Ithaca, N.Y.
Engineering Societies Library, New York, N.Y.
Harvard University, Cambridge, Mass.
Johns Hopkins University, Baltimore, Md.
Joint University Libraries, Nashville, Tenn.
Library of Congress, Washington, D.C.
Massachusetts Institute of Technology, Cambridge, Mass.
University of Michigan, Ann Arbor, Mich.
University of Minnesota, Minneapolis, Minn.
New York Public Library, New York, N.Y.
University of North Carolina, Durham, N.C.
Ohio State University, Columbus, Ohio
University of Oklahoma, Norman, Okla.
Philadelphia Academy of Natural Sciences, Philadelphia, Pa.
Princeton University, Princeton, N.J.
Smithsonian Institution, Washington, D.C.
Stanford University, Stanford, Calif.
U.S. Geological Survey, Washington, D.C.
University of Washington, Seattle, Wash.
Yale University, New Haven, Conn.

A few special collections were noted as follows:

Paleontology: University of Chicago, Chicago, Ill.

[1] Downs, R. B., Leading American Library Collections, *Library Quart.*, Vol. 12, pp. 457–473, 1942.

Vertebrate paleontology:
  American Museum of Natural History, New York, N.Y.
  Princeton University, Princeton, N.J.
Physiography: Columbia University, New York, N.Y.

The chief geologic libraries in each of the states of the United States, Alaska, the provinces of Canada, Newfoundland, Mexico, and Central America are enumerated in "Directory of Geological Material in North America," by J. V. Howell and A. I. Levorsen, *Bulletin of the American Association of Petroleum Geologists*, Vol. 30, No. 8, Pt. 2, August 1946, pp. 1337–1432.

Based upon a report of the American Library Association Board on Resources in American Libraries and upon a joint questionnaire of the Association of American Geographers and the American Society for Professional Geographers,[1] the following libraries in the United States are regarded as the most important for geographic studies and research.[2]

American Geographical Society, New York, N.Y.
University of California, Berkeley, Calif.
University of Chicago, Chicago, Ill.
Clark University, Worcester, Mass.
Columbia University, New York, N.Y.
John Crerar Library, Chicago, Ill.
Explorers' Club, New York, N.Y.
Harvard University, Cambridge, Mass.
Huntington Library, San Marino, Calif.
University of Illinois, Urbana, Ill.
Library of Congress, Washington, D.C.
Louisiana State University, Baton Rouge, La.
University of Michigan, Ann Arbor, Mich.
National Geographic Society, Washington, D.C.
New York Public Library, New York, N.Y.
University of North Carolina, Durham, N.C.
Ohio State University, Columbus, Ohio
Pan American Union, Washington, D.C.
University of Texas, Austin, Tex.
U.S. Department of Agriculture, Washington, D.C.
U.S. Department of Commerce, Washington, D.C.
U.S. Department of State, Washington, D.C.
U.S. Geological Survey, Washington, D.C.
U.S. Weather Bureau, Washington, D.C.
University of Washington, Seattle, Wash.

[1] Downs, R. B., Leading American Library Collections, *Library Quart.*, Vol. 12, pp. 457–473, 1942.

[2] Wright, John Kirtland, and Elizabeth T. Platt, "Aids to Geographical Research," 2d. ed., p. 276, American Geographical Society, New York, 1947.

University of Wisconsin, Madison, Wis.
Yale University, New Haven, Conn.

The largest geographic libraries in the world, according to prewar data, are named on page 66 of "Aids to Geographical Research," by John Kirtland Wright and Elizabeth T. Platt, 2d ed., American Geographical Society, New York, 1947.

The four volumes of "Special Library Resources," edited by Rose L. Vormelker and published by the Special Libraries Association, New York, describe in some detail the resources and facilities of practically all important libraries in the United States and Canada arranged alphabetically, first by states and provinces, next by cities, and then by name of the library or organization. Special collections are entered under headings which include the following: Geology, Geophysics, Geodesy, Geochemistry, Geography, Economic geography, Mineral resources, Industrial minerals, Mines and mining, Mining engineering, Mineralogy, Minerals, Aluminum, Copper, Iron, Molybdenum, Nickel, Sulfur, Zinc. The following table gives the arrangement of the contents.

Volume No.	No. of Libraries	Date	Contents
1	766	1941	All states, less extensive coverage than Vols. 2 and 3
2	844	1946	Alabama to Montana
3	814	1947	Nebraska to Wyoming and Canada
4	...	1947	Cumulative indexes to Vols. 1 to 3

An index to organizations is in each volume; an index to special collections is in Vol. 1; subject indexes to special collections are in Vols. 2 and 3; a personnel index is in Vol. 1.

A subject index to special libraries in the United States and Canada is also included in "American Library Directory," published by R. R. Bowker Company, New York (2d ed., 1948).

The facilities of government depository libraries are discussed in Chap. 10 on United States Government Documents.

United States and Canadian members of the American Institute of Mining and Metallurgical Engineers and the three other "Founder Societies" may borrow any of 150,000 books in the Engineering Societies Library, New York. Three volumes may be borrowed at one time; the borrowing of rare books and reference books is subject to approval by the library board. The other extensive bibliographic services of the library are described by the director, Ralph H. Phelps, in *Mining and Metallurgy* (Vol. 29, pp. 618–619, 1948).

An expansion of the usual library services for research purposes has taken place through the establishment of bibliographic centers, which coordinate regional activities in bibliographic problems. There are three such centers in the country.

> Philadelphia Bibliographical Center and Union Library Catalogue. Fine Arts Building, University of Pennsylvania, Philadelphia, Pa. Region: Philadelphia and adjacent states.
>
> Bibliographical Center for Research, Rocky Mountain Region. Public Library, Denver, Colo. Region: Colorado, Wyoming, Utah, Nebraska, and New Mexico.
>
> Pacific Northwest Bibliographic Center. University of Washington Library, Seattle, Wash. Region: Washington, Oregon, Montana, Idaho, British Columbia.

These bibliographic centers locate publications and manuscripts for libraries and their users, facilitate the borrowing of books among libraries by writing requests to the proper sources, knit the many libraries in the country into a closer system and hence improve local library service, direct those in search of materials on specific subjects to the collections best suited to their purpose, solve bibliographic problems of facts and interpretations, and function as clearinghouses for regional cooperation among libraries in their many activities.

A bibliographic center consists of a collection of bibliographies, catalogues, and reference books useful in identifying and locating books and collections; a trained staff; and a union catalogue, which lists by author in one alphabet publications owned by the libraries in the region and tells where copies are located. In locating materials the bibliographic centers frequently call upon other union catalogues throughout the country, of which the most important is the National Union Catalog at the Library of Congress, Washington, D.C., which records holdings of many of the principal libraries of the United States, Canada, and Europe. "Union Catalogs in the United States," edited by Robert B. Downs and published in 1942 by the American Library Association, Chicago, is a directory of union catalogues and gives other information about them.

The following instructions on how to use the services of a bibliographic center have been issued by the Bibliographical Center for Research, Rocky Mountain Region.

1. Locating Books. If you are seeking particular items and cannot find them in your local library, either apply directly or ask your librarian to request from the nearest bibliographic center the locations for these items. You should give all pertinent information—author, title, place of publication, date, and where you found the reference. The bibliographic center will report where the nearest copies are available.

2. Borrowing Books. If you wish to borrow the items in order to examine them,

ask your local librarian to request them on interlibrary loan.   The librarian should
(a) give complete information, (b) state the name and affiliation of the person who
is to use the book, (c) the purpose of the loan, and (d) indicate the latest date when
the item will still be of use.   The borrowing library pays the postage both ways.
It also agrees to regulations set up to safeguard the book in transit and while being
used.

3. Locating Special Collections.   If you are working on a special problem and
seek a collection which has strong holdings in your field, write to one of the bibliographic centers, stating the subject of your inquiry as precisely as possible.   To
avoid duplication of effort, indicate what steps you have already taken.   The
center to the best of its ability will advise you as to libraries and special collections
suited to your problem.

4. Locating Bibliographies.   If you want to know of bibliographies on a given
subject or a given author, write or visit your bibliographic center.   An effort will
be made either to answer your question directly or to refer you to a library, an institution, or an individual qualified to help you.

The tendency that is apparently increasing to ship books to any but
nearby places by express instead of library-rate parcel post is greatly increasing the cost of borrowing books at a distance, even though such
shipments are supposed to be safer and are more convenient because out-
going packages are called for.

The wartime and postwar fate of the collections of scientific and technical
books in German libraries, the most important in Europe, is exhaustively
presented in "Die deutschen wissenschaftlichen Bibliotheken nach dem
Krieg" by Georg Leyh, published in Tübingen in 1947, by Verlag von
J. C. B. Mohr (Paul Siebeck).   An extensive survey of the contents of this
book was given in a review by Lawrence S. Thompson in *Science* (Vol. 107,
pp. 124–125, Jan. 30, 1948).

PHOTOPRINTS AND MICROFILMS

Photoprinting and, more recently, microfilming have made available
practically all the world's literature to geologists, wherever they are
situated.   Even if the original publication is not too rare or valuable to be
shipped, a photoprint (Photostat is a trade name) or a microfilm may often
be obtained with less expense, especially for a small amount of material,
than the cost involved in a two-way express shipment of the original book
or bound volume of a periodical.

Photoprinting is more common than microfilming; it is especially good
for obtaining copies of illustrations and accurate copies of complicated
tables, charts, diagrams, formulas, or equations, which might be copied
erroneously if done by hand.

Microfilm is an image or copy of film, reduced in size, usually about eight
to thirty times, from the original.   It cannot be read by the unaided eye
but must be read by means of some type of optical projector, which is

usually called a microfilm reading machine, or else projection prints, which are photographic positive enlargements on paper, may be made from the film and read directly.

Microfilms are very economical for long runs or whole books, but photoprints are more convenient and cheaper for short articles up to 10 or 20 pages. The material produced by either of these methods of mechanical reproduction can conveniently be filed.

Most large libraries are equipped to provide photoprints or microfilms. Almost all libraries, moreover, will furnish photoprints at cost through local commercial firms wherever possible.

J. V. Howell and A. I. Levorsen compiled a "Selected List of Libraries Which Furnish Microfilms and Photostats" for the *Bulletin of the American Association of Petroleum Geologists*.[1]

The "List of Periodicals Abstracted" by *Chemical Abstracts* contains a list of 280 libraries in the United States, Canada, Hawaii, and Puerto Rico and indicates which of them provide photoprinting (*P*) or microfilming (*M*) services. The latest list is in Vol. 40, No. 24, Pt. 2, of *Chemical Abstracts*, Dec. 20, 1946, pp. 2–6.

Published in 1947 by the Special Libraries Association, New York, the "Directory of Microfilm Services in the United States and Canada" includes both institutions and commercial sources and tells how to order film. Entries are arranged geographically and alphabetically, first by state, then by city, then by the name of the organization; an index is provided. This book supersedes the "Directory of Microfilm Sources" by Ross C. Cibella, published by the Special Libraries Association in 1941.

Collections of microfilm may be located through "Union List of Microfilms," which is intended to be a listing of all important filming in the United States and Canada, omitting strips judged of minor importance. The library that has the film is indicated by a code, and a complete directory is given. The Basic List was published in 1942 by the Philadelphia Bibliographical Center and Union Library Catalogue, Philadelphia. Five supplements have been issued as follows:

Supplement	Year	Published
1	1942	1943
2	1943	1944
3	1944	1945
4	1945	1946
5	1946	1947

[1] Howell, J. V., and A. I. Levorsen, Directory of Geological Material in North America, *Am. Assoc. Petroleum Geologists Bull.*, Vol. 30, No. 8, Pt. 2, pp. 1334–1336, 1946.

A revised, enlarged, and cumulated edition, including the Basic List, the above supplements, and material received through 1949, was published (lithoprinted) in 1950 by J. W. Edwards, Ann Arbor, Michigan. It covers 159 major libraries and institutions. Entries are alphabetical by author, or by title if the author is unknown; each is preceded by the Library of Congress classification.

Microfilm from abroad can be obtained from one of the following commercial firms.[1]

International Microstat Corporation, 18 West 48 Street, New York 19, N.Y.
Recordak Corporation, 350 Madison Avenue, New York 17, N.Y.
University Microfilms, 313 North First Avenue, Ann Arbor, Mich.

The last-named company publishes semiannually *Microfilm Abstracts*, a compilation of abstracts of doctoral dissertations, the full text of which can be purchased in microfilm. Each issue contains a cumulative index of titles abstracted in preceding issues. Beginning with Vol. 6, No. 2, abstracts of longer monographs were added in addition to theses.

The Library of the U.S. Department of Agriculture conducts a useful Bibliofilm Service which provides both photoprints and microfilms of almost any published material available. Photoprints are usually supplied in a continuous untrimmed strip slightly smaller than the original. Order blanks furnished free by the library require the following information:

For books or pamphlets: author, title, publisher, date, and pages to be copied.
For periodicals or series: author, title, periodical, volume, number, inclusive pages to be copied, and date.

All orders, except by Federal agencies, must be accompanied by full payment in cash, money order, postal note, or check payable to the Treasurer of the United States. Convenient coupons are available from the Library by sending cash, money order, postal note, or check payable to the Treasurer of the United States. Refund for material that cannot be supplied is made by coupons unless payment by check, which requires about 6 weeks, is specifically requested. If the Library cannot supply the material, it is authorized to make the refund to any agency that will supply the copy at or below the prices quoted. By special arrangement members of the American Chemical Society can obtain photocopying of material outside the journal facilities of the Library and even outside the facilities in Washington, D.C. Coupons are provided for these members by the American Chemical Society or the editor of *Chemical Abstracts*.

[1] "Directory of Microfilm Services in the United States and Canada," p. vii, Special Libraries Association, New York, 1947.

The Library of Congress provides a Photoduplication Service to produce copies of materials in its collections that are available for research use. Facsimile prints (Photostats) in negatives or positives, microfilms in negatives or positives, microfilm enlargement prints, photographs (negatives, contact prints, enlargements), lantern slides, blueprints, and Ozalid prints are furnished. Application forms for ordering these duplications can be obtained free upon request to the Photoduplication Service, Library of Congress, Washington. The current price list is printed on the back of the form, and terms similar to those given above for the Library of the Department of Agriculture are specified.

The American Documentation Institute, Washington, which formerly operated the Bibliofilm Service before it was acquired by the Library of the U.S. Department of Agriculture, sells microfilms of out-of-print books, rare books, photographs and other illustrations, and sets of rare and out-of-print journals of a scientific or scholarly nature. Included among the last are *Zeitschrift für Kristallographie*, Vols. 61–100, 1925 to 1939, and a number of chemical periodicals. The Institute also sells both microfilms and photoprints of translations into English of certain scientific papers published in foreign periodicals. A "Catalog of Auxiliary Publications" can be obtained free upon request.

The Engineering Societies Library, New York, supplies Photostats as white-on-black (negative) prints, though black-on-white (positive) prints are also furnished. Members of the American Institute of Mining and Metallurgical Engineers and of the three other Founder Societies receive a price discount. A separate print is required for each large page, but any two facing pages which together measure not over 11 by 14 inches will be photographed as one print. The following information should be given: title of article, name of publication in which it appeared, volume, number, date of publication, and page numbers. Microfilms are available through arrangement with another organization.

The Library of the American Philosophical Society, Philadelphia, maintains a Photoduplication Service for the purpose of supplying 35-mm microfilm copies of out-of-print articles and manuscript material. Enlarged prints are also available.

The Office of Technical Services of the Department of Commerce, Washington, makes available in either Photostat or microfilm form (and a few that are mimeographed) the wartime research reports of the Office of Scientific Research and Development, the Office of Production Research and Development, Army and Navy arsenals and research laboratories, and many other government agencies. Reports are also contributed by various members of the United Nations. Thousands of original German-language documents reporting the wartime work of German scientists and engineers are included, and they are added as received from O.T.S. investigators. About 150,000 reports, comprising several million pages and indexed by almost one million entries, have been issued to July 1950, making this publication "industry's largest single guide to the world's phenomenal scientific and technical progress since 1939." Each report is listed and abstracted in descriptive (not critical) fashion in the *Bibliography of Technical Reports* now issued monthly by the same agency. Before July 1949 the title was *Bibliography of Scientific and Industrial Reports;* from January 1946 to June 1948 it was issued weekly and was free, but subscriptions are now sold by the Superintendent of Documents, Washington (see page 104). A section on Minerals and mineral products is included. Photostats and microfilm should be ordered from the Photoduplication Service, Library of Congress, Washington. Printed reports should be ordered from the Office of Technical Services (O.T.S.), Washington. The individual prices vary considerably, most Photostats running about two to six times as expensive as microfilms. Reports must be ordered by number, and checks should be made payable to the Treasurer of the United States. A descriptive circular is available free upon request. Elaborately cross-referenced subject indexes are issued quarterly, and a 530-page "Numerical Index" to Vols. 1 to 10 (1946 to 1948) was issued in 1950. Short bibliographies on specialized subjects are prepared separately from time to time (see page 56).

A photocopying service is provided in Great Britain by the Science Library. Negatives of pages in periodicals, reduced in size to about 65 per cent, are furnished upon receipt of full bibliographic information. A signed declaration must be submitted that the material will be used for study, research, criticism, or review and not for sale or reproduction. Payment is accepted only in requisition forms purchased in advance.

Proposed projects for microfilming an entire book of average size on a single filing card have been suggested by librarians during recent years. Plans for the extensive adaptation to geologic books of this method of reproduction have been discussed by the Research Committee of the American Association of Petroleum Geologists.[1]

TRANSLATIONS

The importance of translations lies in the contradiction that, although science is international, the world is not yet unified. A classification of geologic literature according to language would correspond only partly to a classification by country. Geologic literature may be expected to appear in practically any language, but the overwhelming majority of it is published in a few of the most widely used languages.

[1] Hanna, Marcus A., Microcard Libraries, *Am. Assoc. Petroleum Geologists Bull.*, Vol. 31, pp. 393-394, 1947.

As mentioned in Chap. 1, Russian has crowded out the foreign languages in Soviet publications. Elsewhere in the world English is being used more and more extensively and is rapidly becoming a second language in France. Swiss publications are partly in German, partly in French, and a few in Italian. Scandinavian publications and those of the Netherlands are apt to be in diverse languages—Dutch, French, English, and German. Bilingual Belgium uses French and Flemish, the former predominating. Some prewar Japanese publications were issued in several European languages (especially German and English) in addition to Japanese, but English is gaining ground there as elsewhere.

The subject of translations brings to attention the importance of foreign-language geologic and other scientific dictionaries. These are discussed in Chap. 15 on Books. An extensive list of abbreviations used in foreign (as well as English) literature is given in "A Guide to the Literature of Chemistry" by Crane and Patterson.[1] Other lists of abbreviations will be found in many English–foreign-language dictionaries.

Some libraries are equipped to furnish translations into English of material published in a foreign language. Other libraries can have translations done by a member of their staff or by an outside person at standard rates. Some commercial translators are available through their advertisements in scientific journals. The best translator is one who is familiar with the technical terminology used in the particular subject concerned. The "List of Periodicals Abstracted" by *Chemical Abstracts* contains a list of 280 libraries in the United States, Canada, Hawaii, and Puerto Rico and indicates which of them provide translating services. The latest list is in Vol. 40, No. 24, Pt. 2, of *Chemical Abstracts*, Dec. 20, 1946, pp. 2–6. A directory of translators is maintained by the Science-Technology Group of the Special Libraries Association.

Translations are supplied at cost by the Engineering Societies Library, New York. The rates charged depend upon the language, and a discount is given to members of the American Institute of Mining and Metallurgical Engineers and the three other Founder Societies. A small additional charge is made for the extra time required for articles that contain a high proportion of formulas or other difficult material. Estimates will be given in advance if requested.

Translations of a number of foreign scientific and scholarly papers are sold in microfilm and photoprint form by the American Documentation Institute, Washington. These are listed by subject in the "Catalog of Auxiliary Publications," which can be obtained free upon request. Twenty

---

[1] Crane, E. J., and Austin M. Patterson, "A Guide to the Literature of Chemistry," pp. 245–257, John Wiley & Sons, Inc., New York, 1927.

industrial firms, as well as other organizations and periodicals, have deposited translations with the Institute.

Edited translations into English of captured German documents now in the custody of the United States Technical Oil Mission and Office of Technical Services are sold by Charles A. Meyer and Company, Inc., New York. A priced catalogue and abstract list can be obtained free upon request.

The Geological Society of America established in 1947 a Committee on Russian Literature (Ronald K. DeFord, chairman) for the purpose of compiling a list of English translations of Russian geologic articles and books available in manuscript form in the United States. This information will be included in the *Bibliography and Index of Geology Exclusive of North America* (see page 57) and the *Bibliography of Economic Geology* (see page 57).

The titles of articles that have been translated from Soviet scientific journals and available at Brookhaven's Central Repository for Translations of Russian Scientific Articles are listed in "A Guide to Russian Scientific Periodical Literature," published by Brookhaven National Laboratory, Upton, New York.[1]

The Translations Pool of the Special Libraries Association is developing a union card index of technical translations which will show the location and availability of known scientific and technical translations of articles and reports from foreign languages into English.[2] The fields to be covered include engineering, materials, aeronautics, chemistry, metallurgy, communications, petroleum, and technology. The Association will not supply actual translations but will act as a clearinghouse to give information as to where certain translations may be obtained, and in cases where organizations do not wish to reveal their interests through disclosure of translations in their files, it will serve as intermediary for loans. A Directory of Translators is also maintained, and about seven regional centers are planned. Inquiries with respect to procedure in using this free service should be addressed to the librarian, Wayne Kalenich, Southwestern Research Institute, San Antonio.

[1] *Science*, Vol. 109, p. 601, 1949.
[2] *Science*, Vol. 107, p. 620, 1948; Vol. 109, p. 601, 1949.

PART III

KINDS OF GEOLOGIC LITERATURE

CHAPTER 7

INDEX GUIDES AND BIBLIOGRAPHIES

These two types of guides to geologic literature—index guides and bibliographies—are discussed together because they are similar in their nature and their use. Both are essentially lists of publications, telling what has been published on certain subjects and where the literature may be found. In both of them, most of the various kinds of literature described in the other chapters of Part III of this book are usually brought together in a single compilation. All index guides are bibliographies, though the reverse statement would not necessarily be valid.

Index guides are, as a whole, the more general in scope of the two, ranging from those which deal with the entire science of geology or a special branch of it to those which cover a wide gamut of subjects, of which geology may constitute only a small part. Indexes to abstracts and abstract journals, though in themselves similar to any other kind of index, really belong in the next chapter, inasmuch as they refer specifically to a single publication or series of publications and do not include material appearing elsewhere; it is the job of the abstract itself to refer adequately to the original source. Index guides, as here considered, are direct references to the original publications.

Index guides may be divided into separate author and subject listings, perhaps with additional lists of localities or other information pertinent to the subject and manner of approach. Or they may be combined into a single comprehensive index, covering all entries in one alphabetical arrangement. The same instructions given in Chap. 5 on indexing in general are applicable to index guides to geologic literature.

Index guides devoted to listing all available material on a given subject or on a range of subjects (no matter how extensive) and issued at more or less regular intervals are known as "index serials." Being issued at intervals, they take on the aspect of periodicals; in this book, for purposes of convenience, they are discussed separately from periodicals because they are essentially a secondary source of publication whereas periodicals function chiefly as primary sources of original material. Some bibliographies, moreover, also appear as periodical publications (that is, at regular intervals), and so this distinction as to time becomes of little importance. Index serials vary considerably in scope, quality, and arrangement, but almost all of them list the author, title, and sufficient other data to enable the reader to locate the original reference.

Some unpublished indexes have been prepared on individual cards, but they are generally inaccessible. Some are in use in certain libraries but then only on limited subjects. The thousands of cards that index the George Frederick Kunz library on gems in the U. S. Geological Survey, Washington, represent the most extensive compilation ever made on that subject. A card index to the quadrangle topographic maps of the U. S. Geological Survey prepared by states and counties by the Cincinnati Public Library is another example of such a valuable but unpublished index.

The Institut international de bibliographie, Brussels, Belgium, has a card index of millions of cards representing all fields of science. Paleontology is eminently covered in the closely subdivided classified card bibliography of paleontology, zoology, and anatomy of the Concilium bibliographicum, Zurich, Switzerland. Several noted card indexes (U. S. Patent Office, E. C. Worden Laboratories) of vast size pertain to patents and so have slight value to the geologist, although they are of inestimable value to chemists, physicists, and engineers; these indexes are similar in content to some of the abstracts discussed in Chap. 8 and some of the reference books discussed in Chap. 15, because they are descriptive lists of patents as much as references to the literature of patents.

Other card indexes, also on special subjects, are in use in industrial or commercial firms or have been prepared by teachers or research workers for their own use. An example known to the author is the card index compiled by Professor Kirk Bryan of Harvard University on many aspects of geology, geomorphology, and geography; its summaries of the contents of the periodical and bulletin literature covered give the index much the character of a classified file of abstracts. This and other similar unpublished indexes are not readily available to the general reader.

A guide to unpublished indexes in libraries, listing them and telling where they may be found, is "Local Indexes in American Libraries. A Union List of Unpublished Indexes," published in 1945 by the F. W. Faxon Company, Boston (221 pp.). It was edited by Norma O. Ireland from a compilation made by the Junior Members Round Table of the American Library Association from about 8,000 indexes in 950 libraries in the United States, Canada, Hawaii, and Puerto Rico. The original indexes vary from card files to typed or mimeographed lists. The book has over 2,500 subject headings, ranging from those which are general and popular to those which are specialized and scholarly. Information given includes the number of entries, the form of entry, where the index is located, and sometimes a brief description of it. This book is based upon and supersedes "Special Indexes in American Libraries," published in 1917 by the American Library Association, Chicago. The following libraries, arranged alphabetically by states, are represented under the headings Geology, Geography, Paleobotany, and Mining.

Denver Public Library, Denver, Colo.
Colorado School of Mines Library, Golden, Colo.
University of Delaware Memorial Library, Newark, Del.
Maine State Library, Augusta, Maine
Enoch Pratt Free Library, Baltimore, Md.
Helena Public Library, Helena, Mont.
Princeton University Library, Princeton, N.J.
New York Public Library, New York, N.Y.
Toledo Public Library, Toledo, Ohio
Tulsa Public Library, Tulsa, Okla.
Carnegie Library of Pittsburgh, Pittsburgh, Pa.
El Paso Public Library, El Paso, Tex.
Fairbanks Museum of Natural History, St. Johnsbury, Vt.
Seattle Public Library, Seattle, Wash.
University of Washington Library, Seattle, Wash.

Separate state lists not included in the above compilation are listed in the same book on page xv; information about them may be obtained from persons in each state whose names are given on pages xiii to xiv.

Lists of current unpublished indexes are included at intervals in the *Bulletin of Bibliography*, which is published three times a year by the F. W. Faxon Company, Boston.

A companion volume to "Local Indexes in American Libraries," dealing with published rather than unpublished indexes, is "An Index to Indexes" by Norma O. Ireland, published in 1942 by the F. W. Faxon Company, Boston (123 pp.). It has over 1,000 indexes to 280 subjects.

The word "bibliography," once confined to books relating to a particular subject, has undergone as great a change as the word "dilapidated." Bibliographies are now merely lists of references on a given subject or by a given author. Bibliographies that are annotated to any extent take on the character of abstracts such as those discussed in the next chapter.

Entries in a bibliography may be arranged alphabetically according to author, chronologically according to date, in sequence according to relative importance, or grouped according to type of publication (such as book, periodical, etc.) or subject, perhaps by an arbitrary code or other classification. Many combinations are possible in extensive bibliographies, and examples of many different arrangements are known in the literature. The reader should first survey the arrangement of a chosen bibliography before trying to use it. Large bibliographies are themselves often indexed, especially if they are not classified.

Inasmuch as the subject under consideration has already been specified, the most important entry in subject bibliography is complete information as to the exact place where the reference is to be found. Periodical references therefore include the name of the publication, the series (if any), the volume or year, and the page. Bulletin references include the name of the issuing agency, the series or other complete designation, the number, and the year. Book references include the volume (if issued in more than one), the publisher, the year or edition number, and the page. Additional information usually considered minimum in a bibliography includes the name of the author and the title of the article, bulletin, or book. Annotations are, as mentioned before, an approach to abstracts, and they are usually valuable and timesaving when employed.

Bibliographies are published in many forms, so that locating them is a serious problem. Excellent bibliographies of the best references are often found appended to articles in the better general or special encyclopedias and in reviews, as discussed in Chap. 2 on Conducting the Search.

The best bibliographies of a specific subject should be expected in books on that subject, including textbooks, but this great expectation sometimes proves a disappointment for reasons that are not always noble. The references that are listed in some books represent those to which the author is willing to admit his indebtedness, and these by occasional coincidence may not include publications of his chief rivals in scientific publication. Bibliographies in books do not necessarily occur at the end of the book but may be found at the end of a chapter or at the end of a section within the chapter.

Monographs are a good place to find bibliographies on the subjects concerned; in fact, a bibliography superior in both quality and quantity should be a required part of any definitive monograph or treatise. Especially thorough bibliographies are a feature of German books of the Handbuch type.

Most libraries will prepare special bibliographies, with or without charge. The Engineering Societies Library, New York, makes moderate charges. The Technical Department of the Tulsa Public Library has assembled important bibliographies on various phases of the petroleum industry. Individuals or firms doing such work advertise in the general scientific periodicals of wide circulation, such as *Science*.

The Office of Technical Services, Department of Commerce, Washington, offers assistance to subscribers to the *Bibliography of Technical Reports* (and presumably to others) in compiling bibliographies from its huge number of reports in all fields of science and technology (see page 46). A master card file is maintained, cross-indexing all reports by subject, author, title, and agency of origin. Short bibliographies on specialized subjects are prepared separately from time to time. The only one of geologic interest to July 1950 is the "Bibliography of Reports on Iron Ore," listing 15 reports and the prices at which they are available in microfilm and Photostat. The original documents are deposited at the Library of Congress and can be inspected at the Annex Reading Room if a reproduction is not wanted for purchase.

The Research Information Service of the National Research Council, discontinued in 1935, possessed a card index of over 30,000 bibliographies on all scientific subjects.

The unpublished bibliographies of geology and related sciences discussed in Chap. 18 might appropriately be referred to here.

Scattered bibliographies are found in each of the types of publication discussed in the succeeding chapters of this book. To assist in finding them, a class of publications known as "bibliographies of bibliographies" has arisen. The complexity of modern research into the literature is shown by the existence of "bibliographies of bibliographies of bibliographies." The next part of this chapter is a small example of one, discussing compilations of particular use to the geologist. Index guides are described first.

General geology

The most generally used index guide to geologic literature is *Bibliography of North American Geology*, published at intervals by the U. S. Geological Survey. It includes all aspects of general geology written by Americans and specifically covers the geology of the continent of North America, including the United States, Canada and Newfoundland, Greenland, the Arctic region north of the continent, Mexico, Central America, Panama, the West Indies, and Trinidad; the Hawaiian Islands and Guam are also represented. The writings of foreign authors are not included except those appearing in American publications. The entries are listed under the names of the authors, which are arranged alphabetically. This author list is followed by a comprehensive subject index.

This series of publications at present covers the years 1785 to 1948 in nine *Bulletins* of the U. S. Geological Survey, as shown in the chart on page 58.

Bibliography and Index of Geology Exclusive of North America has been published since 1934 by the Geological Society of America, New York. It is one of the major guides to geologic literature, covering all the world outside the North American continent, Panama, the West Indies, Greenland, as well as Hawaii and Guam. Hence it complements the Survey's *Bibliography of North American Geology*. Material on foreign geology by North American geologists is included. Entries are arranged alphabetically by author; an extensive subject index constitutes more than one-quarter of each volume. If a paper has titles in more than one language, all titles are usually given, but a Cyrillic title is omitted if accompanied by one in a Roman alphabet.

The notes accompanying many of the entries give this publication some

Bul-letin	Title	Compiler	Date	Supersedes
746	"Geologic Literature on North America, 1785–1918," Part I, Bibliography	John M. Nickles	1923 (1924)	*Bulletin* 44 (1886); *Bulletin* 75 (1887–1889); *Bulletin* 91 (1890); *Bulletin* 99 (1891); *Bulletin* 127 (cumulating *Bulletins* 44, 75, 91, 99, 1732–1891); *Bulletin* 130 (1892–1893); *Bulletin* 135 (1894); *Bulletin* 146 (1895); *Bulletin* 149 (1896); *Bulletin* 156 (1897); *Bulletin* 162 (1898); *Bulletin* 172 (1899); *Bulletins* 188 and 189 (cumulating
747	"Geologic Literature on North America, 1785–1918," Part II, Index	John M. Nickles	1924	*Bulletins* 130, 135, 146, 149, 156, 162, 172, 1892–1900); *Bulletin* 203 (1901); *Bulletin* 221 (1902); *Bulletin* 240 (1903); *Bulletin* 271 (1904); *Bulletin* 301 (cumulating *Bulletins* 203, 221, 240, 271, 1901–1905); *Bulletin* 372 (1906–1907); *Bulletin* 409 (1908); *Bulletin* 444 (1909); *Bulletin* 495 (1910); *Bulletin* 524 (1911); *Bulletin* 545 (1912); *Bulletin* 584 (1913); *Bulletin* 617 (1914); *Bulletin* 645 (1915); *Bulletin* 665 (1916); *Bulletin* 684 (1917); *Bulletin* 698 (1918)
823	"Bibliography of North American Geology, 1919–1928"	John M. Nickles	1931	*Bulletin* 731 (1919–1920); *Bulletin* 758 (1921–1922); *Bulletin* 784 (1923–1924); *Bulletin* 802 (1925–1926);
937	"Bibliography of North American Geology, 1929–1939"	Emma Mertins Thom	1944	*Bulletin* 834 (1929–1930); *Bulletin* 858 (1931–1932); *Bulletin* 869 (1933–1934); *Bulletin* 892 (1935–1936)
938	"Bibliography of North American Geology for 1940 and 1941"	Emma Mertins Thom	1942 (1943)	
949	"Bibliography of North American Geology, 1942 and 1943"	Emma Mertins Thom	1945 (1946)	
952	"Bibliography of North American Geology, 1944 and 1945"	Emma Mertins Thom	1947	
958	"Bibliography of North American Geology, 1946 and 1947"	Emma Mertins Thom, Marjorie Hooker, and Ruth Reece Dunaven	1949	
968	"Bibliography of North American Geology, 1948"	Emma Mertins Thom, Marjorie Hooker, and Ruth Reece Dunaven	1950	

of the characteristics of an abstract journal; however, although some of the abstracts are as full as some of those in certain abstract journals, most are very brief (merely subtitles), and some entries do not have any amplifying note. This publication is therefore placed in this chapter instead of the next.

Volumes published to date are the following.

Volume	Year covered	Date published	Compilers
1	1933	1934	John M. Nickles and Robert B. Miller
2	1934	1935	John M. Nickles and Robert B. Miller
3	1935	1936	John M. Nickles, Marie Siegrist, Eleanor Tatge
4	1936	1937	John M. Nickles, Marie Siegrist, Eleanor Tatge
5	1937	1938	John M. Nickles, Marie Siegrist, Eleanor Tatge
6	1938	1939	John M. Nickles, Marie Siegrist, Eleanor Tatge
7	1939	1940	John M. Nickles, Marie Siegrist, Eleanor Tatge
8	1940	1941	John M. Nickles, Marie Siegrist, Eleanor Tatge
9	1941–1942	1943	John M. Nickles, Marie Siegrist, Eleanor Tatge
10	1943–1944	1946	John M. Nickles, Marie Siegrist, Eleanor Tatge
11	1945–1946	1947	Marie Siegrist and Eleanor Tatge
12	1947	1948	Marie Siegrist and Eleanor Tatge
13	1948	1949	Marie Siegrist and Eleanor Tatge

Published annually from 1895 to 1936 and covering the years 1894 to 1934, the *List of Geological Literature Added to the Geological Society's Library during the Year* . . . was a comprehensive listing, alphabetically by author and title, of articles in periodicals, books, and other types of geologic publications acquired by the Geological Society, London. The title varied and 37 volumes were published in 25 volumes. A subject index was issued (separately from 1920 to 1924).

Beginning in July 1923 *Bibliographie des sciences géologiques* has been published quarterly by the Société géologique de France, listing by subject all works on geology currently received at certain French libraries. An author index is included. Since 1948 Section 8 of *Bulletin analytique* (described below) has superseded the geologic material in this publication.

Bulletin analytique is a monthly bibliography which attempts to list or abstract briefly the world's literature of science and technology, both periodicals and books. It has been published in Paris since 1940 by the Centre de documentation du centre national de la recherche scientifique. Section 8 covers Geology, mineralogy, petrography, and paleontology. Section 4 includes Crystallography. In addition to the complete volumes, 12 sections, including the two above, are issued separately.

Seismology

Bibliography of Seismology has been published since 1929 by the Dominion Astronomical Observatory, Ottawa. It is an index to pure and applied seismology and related subjects published in periodicals, bulletins, and books. Each number covers a 3-month period. Entries are arranged alphabetically by author and numbered consecutively in each issue. This publication is a continuation of the *Bibliographical Bulletin* issued from 1926 to 1929 by the Eastern Section of the Seismological Society of America and reprinted in the *Bulletin of the Seismological Society of America*, 1927 to 1929.

Geography

Bibliographie géographique internationale is a comprehensive bibliography of current geographic publications, covering articles in periodicals, bulletins, books, and maps. It is divided into two parts, general and regional, the former including geologic subjects such as geology, geophysics, and geomorphology. A number of geographic societies collaborate in the selection of material. The American Geographical Society, New York, supplies the titles and brief critiques of United States publications and is the distributor in the United States and Canada. This publication was issued, normally annually, from 1891 to 1939 and was resumed in 1948 with inclusion of literature covering the war years. It has also appeared under the title *Bibliographie géographique* (1915 to 1931); the early volumes (1891 to 1914) were either included in *Annales de géographie* or issued as separate numbers of that periodical.

Current Geographical Publications is published by the American Geographical Society, New York. It lists, classified by subject and region, the literature of all types, including maps, added to the Society's Research Catalogue, including articles in periodicals, bulletins, books, and maps. A "Photograph Supplement" lists photographs selected for their geographic value. This publication is mimeographed and has been issued monthly except July and August, with an annual index, since 1938.

Superseding the lists published before 1918 in *The Geographical Journal* are those in *Recent Geographical Literature, Maps, and Photographs Added to the Society's Collections*, published in London from 1918 to 1940 by the Royal Geographical Society. An index to Vols. 1 to 4 (1918 to 1932) was published in 1936.

Geographic literature, especially maps and German publications, is thoroughly listed in *Petermanns geographische Mitteilungen*, published monthly in Gotha by Justus Perthes since 1855. The title until 1938 was *Dr. A. Petermanns Mitteilungen aus Justus Perthes' geographischen Anstalt*. Decennial indexes, including author indexes, were published until 1904; the last index covered 1905 to 1934.

Another German publication with lists of geographic literature was *Bibliotheca geographica: Jahresbibliographie der geographischen Literatur*, published from 1895 to 1917 by Gesellschaft für Erdkunde zu Berlin. It covered the years 1891 to 1910 and superseded the lists published annually from 1853 to 1890 in *Zeitschrift der Gesellschaft für Erdkunde zu Berlin*. An author index was included.

Mining

Bulletin of the Institution of Mining and Metallurgy, London, has been published since 1904. It is an index of material taken from British, American, and Canadian publications in the library of the Institution. Entries are arranged in groups and then listed alphabetically by subject as follows: Assaying and chemistry, Coal, Copper, Economics of mining and metallurgy, Geology, Mineralogy, Ore deposits, Gold, Iron and steel, Lead and zinc, Metallurgy (general), Milling and concentration, Mining (general), Minor metals, Nometallic minerals, Petroleum and natural gas, Plant and power, Precious stones, Silver, Tin.

The Mining World Index of Current Literature was published semiannually from 1912 to 1916 (in 10 volumes) from the international index to mining literature appearing weekly in *Mining and Engineering World*. The entries were classified by subjects, and some were brief abstracts. The authors and subjects were indexed.

"Index of Mining Engineering Literature," by Walter R. Crane, was published in two volumes by John Wiley & Sons, Inc., New York, 1909 to 1912. It covers American and English material and some Australian and Canadian works, including periodicals, bulletins, and books. Volume 1 indexes 18 publications from 1878 to 1907. Volume 2 indexes 26 periodicals completely and 40 other publications (including books) incompletely. It has a classified arrangement with an alphabetical index.

General science and technology, including geology

General, including geology. Intended to cover applied science in a manner equivalent to the *International Catalogue of Scientific Literature* (see page 62), *Mededeelingen van het Nederlandsch Instituut voor Documentatie en Registratuur* was begun in 1922 and published bimonthly by the Nederlandsch Instituut von Documentatie sponsored by the Nederlandsch Instituut voor Efficiency. It covers the technical aspects of geology, including mining, gas and oil technology, fuels, etc. Numbering about 16,000 entries per year, classified by the Universal decimal classification of the Institut international de bibliographie, the entries were intended to be cut out and mounted on cards.[1]

The above publication is a descendant of the *Index of the Technical Press*, begun in 1903 by the Institut international de bibliographie at

[1] *Nature*, Vol. 124, p. 942, 1929.

Brussels. This was also issued under the names *Index de la presse technique* and *Index der technischen Press*. From 1904 to 1921 it was named *Revue de l'ingénieur et index technique* and issued in three editions, French, German, and English, the last (also published in Brussels) being called the *Engineering Press Monthly Index Review*.

Scientific and technical bibliographies and bibliographies of bibliographies taken from the originals in the Engineering Societies Library were listed in various past issues of *Special Libraries* and as supplements thereto under the title "Recent Technical Bibliographies" by Raymond N. Brown.

Technische Zeitschriftenschau has been published weekly since 1916 by Verein deutscher Ingenieure, Berlin and Leipzig. It lists periodical articles and books of technical and engineering interest, classified by subject. The issues from 1924 to 1925 included "Bibliographia technica."

Catalogue of Scientific Papers was published by the Royal Society of London and printed by C. J. Clay & Sons, London, 1867 to 1902, and by the Cambridge University Press, London, 1914 to 1925. All scientific papers published in 1,555 periodicals and bulletins during the nineteenth century are assumed to be included. They are listed alphabetically by authors. The 19 volumes appeared as follows:

Series	Volume No.	Years covered
First	1–6	1800–1863
Second	7–8	1864–1873
Third	9–11	1874–1883
Supplementary	12	1800–1883
Fourth	13–19	1884–1890

These series were complemented by the *Catalogue of Scientific Papers 1800–1900 Subject Index*, publication of which began in 1908 with Vol. 1 and continued to 1914 (3 vols. in 4). This was a separate subject index for each of the 17 branches of science dealt with in the *International Catalogue of Scientific Literature* (see below) and is classified by the same system. The name was changed in 1900 to *International Catalogue of Scientific Literature*, which includes books.

International Catalogue of Scientific Literature was published annually for the years 1901 (published in 1902) to 1914 (completed in 1921) by the Royal Society of London for the International Council. It is a practically complete list of all purely scientific books and articles in periodicals; there is a list of 4,673 periodicals in the 1903 and 1904 supplements. Section *G* of the 17 parts was Mineralogy (including Petrology and Crystallography; 14 vols. in 13); Section *H* was Geology (14 vols.); Section *J* was Geography

(14 vols. in 13); Section *K* was Paleontology (14 vols.). Annual author and subject indexes were published. Each class is in one or two volumes, which contain instructions, a schedule of classification and an index (both of them in English, French, German, and Italian), an author catalogue, and a closely classified subject catalogue. The German titles were published as *Bibliographie der deutschen naturwissenschaftlichen Literatur,* covering 1901 to 1914. The French titles were published as *Bibliographie scientifique française mensuelle,* covering 1901 to 1918.

"A Bibliography of American Natural History: The Pioneer Century, 1769–1865," by Max Meisel, was published by Premier Publishing Company, Brooklyn, in 1924. It contains an annotated bibliography of the publications relating to the history, biography, and bibliography of American science and scientific institutions, with subject and geographic indexes and a bibliography of the biographies and bibliographies of the scientists.

Reportorium commentationum a societatibus litterariis editarum: Secundum disciplinarum ordinem digessit, by Jeremias D. Reuss, is a bibliography of periodical articles and organization bulletins from 1665 to 1800. It was published in Göttigen in 16 volumes from 1801 to 1821. Volume 1 covers "Historia naturalis, generalis et zoologica," Vol. 2 is "Botanica et mineralogia," Vol. 3 is "Chemia et res metallica," and Vol. 4 is "Physica."

Science and technology: other sciences

Index guides and bibliographies pertaining to chemistry, physics, and agriculture are described below.

Chemistry. "Bibliography of Bibliographies on Chemistry and Chemical Technology 1900–1924," compiled by Clarence J. West and D. D. Berolzheimer, was published in Washington in 1925 as *National Research Council Bulletin* 50 (308 pp.). The contents are arranged alphabetically according to the following outline: general bibliographies, abstract journals and yearbooks, general indexes of serials, bibliographies on special subjects, and personal bibliographies.

A first supplement of 161 pages, covering 1924 to 1928, was issued in 1929, and a second supplement of 150 pages, covering 1929 to 1931, was published in 1932.

"List of Manuscript Bibliographies in Chemistry and Chemical Technology," by Clarence J. West and Callie Hull, was published in Washington in 1922 as No. 36 of the Reprint and Circular Series of the National Research Council (17 pp.) Entries are alphabetically arranged according to subject, indicating the period covered and the stage of completeness.

"A Reference List of Bibliographies: Chemistry, Chemical Technology, and Chemical Engineering since 1900," by Julian A. Sohon and William L. Schaaf, was published in 1924 by the H. W. Wilson Company, New York.

It has about 2,000 entries on 647 subjects, alphabetically arranged. Information is given for finding each bibliography.

Section 1 of "A Select Bibliography of Chemistry, 1492–1892," and its supplements, by Henry Carrington Bolton, is a list of chemical bibliographies. These are enumerated on pages 1 to 37 and page 1165 of *Publication* 850, which is Vol. 36 of the Smithsonian Miscellaneous Collections, published in 1893 by the Smithsonian Institution; on pages 1 to 11 of *Publication* 1170, which is Article 7 of Vol. 39 (of the same series), published in 1899 as "A Select Bibliography of Chemistry, 1492–1897, First Supplement" (covering 1893 to 1897 and items previously omitted); and on pages 1 to 5 of *Publication* 1440, which is part of Vol. 44, published in 1904 as "A Select Bibliography of Chemistry, 1492–1902, Second Supplement" (covering 1898 to 1902).

Physics. "Classified List of Published Bibliographies in Physics, 1910–1922," by Karl K. Darrow, is *Bulletin* 47 of the National Research Council, published in 1924 (102 pp.).

Of some indirect interest to geologists is the "List of Manuscript Bibliographies in Astronomy, Mathematics, and Physics," compiled by Clarence J. West and Callie Hull and published in 1923 as No. 41 of the Reprint and Circular Series of the National Research Council (14 pp.).

Agriculture. *The Agricultural Index* has been published monthly since 1917 by the H. W. Wilson Company, New York. It indexes bulletins, books, and the contents of 115 periodicals. Entries are alphabetical by subject. Cumulations are issued in December, February, April, and June, with an annual volume in October. Three-year cumulations replace the annual volume each third year. The series is now made up of Vol. 1, 1916 to 1918; Vol. 2, 1919 to 1921; Vol. 3, 1922 to 1924; Vol. 4, 1925 to 1927; Vol. 5, 1928 to 1930; Vol. 6, 1931 to 1933; Vol. 7, 1934 to 1936; Vol. 8, January 1937 to September 1939; Vol. 9, October 1939 to September 1942; Vol. 10, October 1942 to September 1945; Vol. 11, October 1945 to August 1948.

General literature, including geology

"Contents-Subject Index to General and Periodical Literature," by A. Cotgreave, London, 1900, has a number of geologic entries for books and periodical literature.

Microfilm

"The Union List of Microfilms," which is a list of microfilms and a basic list of holdings in the United States and Canada, is described at length in the section on photoprints and microfilms (pages 43 to 47).

Theses

Lists of theses and collections of abstracts are given in "Guide to Bibliography of Theses," by Thomas R. Palfrey and Henry E. Coleman; this publication is described more fully in Chap. 17 on Theses.

Sources of bibliographies

Bibliographies on geology are indexed in the *Annotated Bibliography of Economic Geology*, which is published by the Economic Geology Publishing Company, Urbana, Illinois. This publication is described in fuller detail in Chap. 8 on Abstracts.

Published bibliographies on mineralogical subjects (considered broadly) are listed and described briefly in abstract fashion in *Mineralogical Abstracts*. This publication is discussed at greater length in the next chapter on Abstracts.

"Catalogue of Published Bibliographies in Geology, 1896–1920," compiled by Edward B. Mathews, is *Bulletin* 36 (Vol. 6, Pt. 5, 228 pp.) of the National Research Council, published in 1923. It is practically a continuation of de Margerie's "Catalogue des bibliographies géologiques" (see below), which gives references up to 1895. There are 3,699 titles, arranged alphabetically by subjects in three groups—general, special, and personal.

Number 27 of the Reprint and Circular Series of the National Research Council is the "List of Manuscript Bibliographies in Geology and Geography," compiled by Homer P. Little from information furnished by members of the Geological Society of America and published in February 1922 (17 pp.). The 144 bibliographies, in manuscript or card index form, are listed according to subject and are described.

A major source of bibliographic information on geology is "Catalogue des bibliographies géologiques" by Emmanuel de Margerie, published in Paris in 1896 by the International Geologic Congress (Gauthiers-Villars et fils). In the 753 pages are 3,918 entries, including publications of all types. The contents are classified; author and subject indexes are included. This book was succeeded by the "Catalogue of Published Bibliographies in Geology, 1896–1920" by E. B. Mathews (see above).

A catalogue of geographic bibliographies, published in 1881, is "Liste provisoire de bibliographies géographiques spéciales" by James Jackson, published in Paris by the Société de géographie.

Other bibliographies in geology and related sciences are listed in some of the important reference books on bibliography enumerated in Chap. 15.

The Engineering Societies Library, New York, will supply bibliographies to members of the American Institute of Mining and Metallurgical Engi-

neers and the three other Founder Societies.   Most other libraries will prepare bibliographies and similar lists within a reasonable limit of their
facilities.

Some of the larger libraries have published lists of the bibliographies that
have been compiled in printed, processed, typewritten, or card-index form
for their own use and that of their readers; there seems to be no available
catalogue of such lists, except that those appearing currently are entered
in the *Bibliographic Index* and similar index-guide publications described
in this chapter.   A well-known list of bibliographies on scientific subjects
is that of the John Crerar Library, Chicago.

Numerous current bibliographies on geology appear regularly in *Bibliographic Index.   A Cumulative Bibliography of Bibliographies*, published
since 1937 by the H. W. Wilson Company, New York.   Arranged in one
alphabetical list by subject are world-wide lists of bibliographies of widely
varying length that have appeared as books or bulletins and in books,
bulletins, and about 1,500 periodicals.   Books are entered by author;
periodicals and bulletins are entered by title.   For the bibliography of an
author, the author is regarded as the subject.   Complete or comprehensive
bibliographies are starred (*) and listed first under the subject.   The titles
used are those of the article, bulletin, or book, but the page references are
for the bibliographies only.   Frequently, of course, a bibliography covers a
wider field than one might infer from the title of a book.   This publication
is issued quarterly, with annual and 5-year cumulations.   A 6-year cumulation for 1937 to 1942 and a 2-year cumulation for 1943 to 1944 are also
available.

Bibliographies on numerous subjects appear in the *Bulletin of Bibliography*, published three times a year by the F. W. Faxon Company,
Boston.   Starting in 1897, a total of 19 volumes have been issued.   Most of
the numbers are still in print; prices are available on application.   All
bibliographies listed in this periodical since the beginning in January 1937
of *Bibliographic Index* (described above) have been included in the latter
publication.   Bibliographies that were published by libraries prior to 1898,
the year after the establishment of the *Bulletin of Bibliography*, are indexed in *New York State Library Bulletin: Bibliography No.* 14, 1898, pp.
367–428 ("Index to Subject Bibliographies in Library Bulletins to December 31, 1897" by Alice N. Nachtmann).

Bibliographies prepared and published by the Division of Bibliography
of the Library of Congress are listed among the other publications of the
Library of Congress in the *Annual Report of the Librarian of Congress*.
These are now indexed in *Bibliographic Index* (see above) and are entered in the catalogues of the Superintendent of Documents (see page 105).

A comprehensive classified catalogue of bibliographies in French scientific and other publications, with an exhaustive index to subjects and authors, is *Bulletin de documentation bibliographique*, issued eight times yearly by the Bibliothéque nationale, Paris. Bibliographies in the publications of other countries are less thoroughly covered.

"Manuel de bibliographie général," by Henri Stein, was published by Picard, Paris, in 1897. It contains 17 chapters, each divided into "sections," which may be further subdivided into "divisions." Chapter 8, Sciences pures, includes Géologie et mineralogie; Chap. 9 is Sciences appliquées; Chap. 12 is Sciences géographiques. Not all the divisions are listed in the plan of contents, but there is a subject index. This book was supplemented by lists appearing in "Le Bibliographie moderne," edited by Henri Stein.

"A Bibliography of Latin American Bibliographies," by C. K. Jones, was published by the Library of Congress (2d ed., 1942) as No. 2 in its Latin-American Series. The bibliographies are arranged alphabetically by countries, Central American countries being grouped together. Geologic entries are listed in the index.

CHAPTER 8

ABSTRACTS

More than a mere listing of author, subject, and title is desirable if the reader is to get full benefit from the work and publications of others. Originating in the reviews and summaries of lectures, articles, and books first published in late eighteenth century scientific periodicals, abstracts developed into a specialized form of guide to scientific literature in the early nineteenth century and have since increased in number and scope. Abstracts are annotated references to the literature and have the following characteristics.

1. Abstracts note the identity of the source publication with as much exactness as can be expected in a regular index guide, giving also as many of the bibliographic data as are stated in the publication itself and adding whatever may have been omitted but may be available through search or inquiry. A complete periodical reference might include the author's name, title, date stated, actual date of publication, and section, part, or other designation. A book reference might include the author's name, title, edition, publisher's name and town, date, paging, price, and cataloguing or classification numbers.

2. Abstracts augment the title, if it is inadequate, in order to give a more comprehensive idea of the subject. Books, unlike articles in periodicals, often have a subtitle or secondary title which appears on the title page even if nowhere else and is copied onto the catalogue cards prepared by professional bibliographers and librarians. These additional titles are often very useful in estimating the purpose and scope of a book. Titles in foreign languages are often translated, the English or other version being placed in brackets after the original title.

3. Abstracts summarize the contents of the publication, with special emphasis on new discoveries, methods, and theories. This is their chief function, the only one that cannot successfully be performed by the other types of bibliographic services. To be done to perfection, such an abstract must be prepared by an expert, one who has a thorough grasp of the field involved, who has the rare combination of impartiality and critical judgment, and who has the skills of analysis and condensation. The significant subjects, words, and phrases are in some abstracts given emphasis by being set in a different type style (boldface or italics) from the rest of the connecting words, or perhaps the abstract is divided into paragraphs.

The impossible task that the abstractor faces in trying to give proper emphasis to the subjects and viewpoints which may later prove to be the ones that will be the most useful is indicated by an article written by the author of this book. A year after being published, some facts and an opinion in it were praised by another worker in the subject. But these things had not even been mentioned in either of the two abstracts published meanwhile.

Abstracts furnished by the author and printed at the beginning of articles in periodicals or contributions to bulletins are often taken directly into abstract periodicals on the assumption that they have been well prepared by the author and approved by his editor. An abstract can be especially useful if it gives space to a publication in proportion to two factors—its importance and its inaccessibility (meaning that foreign and obscure literature is abstracted at greater length). The abstractors can assess the significance of a publication to the great advantage of the reader.

Classifying the abstracts suitably is an important first step in making them available. The various headings and the order in which they are arranged are different in each of the abstracting publications, and an effort should be made to become familiar with them before proceeding further. Books are sometimes grouped together, the subject being indicated only in the index; sometimes book reviews are referred to for a more extensive summary and analysis than the abstract itself offers. Bulletins are likewise covered in most abstracting publications, usually being included with books. Valuable cross references are often given to other abstracts in the same or different classifications that have appeared either in the same issue of the abstracting publication or in previous issues. The arrangement in three abstract journals, *Chemical Abstracts, British Chemical Abstracts,* and *Chemisches Zentralblatt,* is given on pages 57 to 59 of "Library Guide for the Chemist" by Byron A. Soule (McGraw-Hill Book Company, Inc., New York, 1938).

Supplementing the classification and grouping of abstracts are the indexes. These are the more important the larger the number of abstracts and the more interrelated they are in subject coverage, so that placing an abstract under a single heading in the classification is not sufficient. One of the purposes of emphasizing significant words or items by putting them in italics or boldface is to assure their entry in the index. Abstracts that are not thus treated must be read carefully by the indexer in order to get every worth-while entry. In either case the indexes are a very essential part of abstract publications, and deficiencies or errors are a serious handicap to the reader. Periodic and cumulative indexes are most useful in reducing the amount of work involved in any search of the literature; accuracy in compiling is, of course, vital, for a single omission may be fatal to the individual concerned with it.

Subject and author indexes are the essential indexes in geologic abstracts.

Included in subject indexes are localities, materials, processes, products, and persons who are discussed. Abstracts in chemistry and engineering may include formula and patent indexes.

Inasmuch as abstracts are, as already stated, historically an outgrowth of summaries and reviews, there is no sharp distinction among these three kinds of literature. A certain number of publications are devoted exclusively to abstracts—their independent establishment and growth is a desirable trend—and these publications are easy to identify. Other publications, especially periodicals, contain abstracts (either regularly or occasionally) in special sections or "departments," or else they may be printed more or less haphazardly when the opportunity presents itself; such publications are virtually unlimited in number and cannot conveniently be enumerated.

No abstracting publication could possibly be complete unless there were only one printing establishment in the world. Assembling all the publications that are published around the globe and in many languages is a formidable task, even in a limited field. To make the burden lighter, some abstracting organizations arrange for the exchange of abstracts with other similar groups. An abstract publication can, in a way, be incomplete if the individual abstracts are not thoroughly prepared, even if every item that has been published has been found and included.

GEOLOGIC SCIENCES

General geology

Most of the entries in the *Bibliography and Index of Geology Exclusive of North America*, described in the previous chapter, are accompanied by annotations, some of which are full enough to qualify as abstracts.

An excellent geologic abstract journal was *Geologisches Zentralblatt*, which was published from 1901 to 1942 by Gebrüder Borntraeger in Berlin (Vol. 69 being dated 1941–1942). When copied from elsewhere, the abstracts are given in the language of the original abstract rather than in that of the article itself; abstracts written specifically for this publication are in German. *Abteilung A: Geologie*, issued semimonthly, contains abstracts under various headings, including Petrography, Economic deposits, Soil science, Fuel science, Meteoritics, Geophysics, General geology, Volcanism, Hydrology, Regional geology, Geological maps, Glacial geology, Stratigraphy, and Miscellaneous. *Abteilung B: Palaeontologie*, also called *Palaeontologisches Zentralblatt*, was issued monthly. Abstracts in both sections are numbered consecutively for each volume, which has an author index and a subject index. Cumulative indexes have been issued for Vols. 1 to 15 (1901 to 1911), Vols. 16 to 30 (1911 to 1924), and Vols. 31 to 50 (1924 to 1933). In 1943 these publications merged with *Neues Jahrbuch für Mineralogie, Geologie und Paläontologie. Referate* to become *Zentralblatt für Mineralogie, Geologie und Paläontologie* (in three parts), but the permanency of these postwar names is not to be depended upon. The publisher is E. Schweizerbart'sche Verlagsbuchhandlung (Erwin Nägele), Stuttgart.

Neues Jahrbuch . . . itself was issued in three sections: (1) Crystallography and mineralogy, (2) General geology, petrography, geochemistry, economic geology, and (3) Historical and regional geology, paleontology. It was begun in 1807 and appeared under other names until 1830, when it began to adopt names similar to its last one, which continued from 1862 until the merger with *Geologisches Zentralblatt* in 1943.

Another geologic abstract journal is *Revue de géologie et des sciences connexes*, published since 1920 (except during the Second World War) by Société géologique de Liége, Belgium. Abstracts that are copied are in the language originally used. Headings, given in French, English, Italian, and German, include the following: Mineralogy and crystallography, Petrography and lithology, General geology, Seismology, Vulcanology, Tectonics, Hydrology, Glacial geology, Stratigraphy, Physiographical geology, Regional geology, Maps, Industrial geology and economic deposits, Study of soils and agrogeology, General paleontology, Paleobotany, Paleozoology, and Miscellaneous. Each volume has an author index, a geographic index, and a subject index.

Bulletin analytique, described in Chap. 7, includes many entries which are short abstracts of the literature of geology and its branches.

Economic geology

Annotated Bibliography of Economic Geology consists of valuable abstracts (and indexes to them) in the broad field of economic geology. It has been published since 1929 by the Economic Geology Publishing Company, Urbana, Illinois. The National Research Council sponsored the work until July 1, 1936, and the Society of Economic Geologists has done so since. Each issue is divided into about 35 or 40 sections and subsections, which vary from time to time. The abstracting is done by about the same number of individual abstractors under the editorship of about a dozen section chiefs. Volume 1 (1929, covering 1928) consisted of one double-size issue; succeeding volumes contain two semiannual numbers. A general index to Vols. 1 to 10 (1928 to 1938) was published in 1939.

Many abstracts on the mineralogy and geology of diamonds, other abrasives, refractories, and hard metals are included in *Bibliography of Industrial Diamond Applications*, published monthly since 1944 by the Industrial Diamond Information Bureau, London. Prior to 1944 it was called *Bibliography of Diamond Tools and Related Subjects*.

Geophysics

A specialized abstract publication in geology is "Geophysical Abstracts." It covers world literature on geophysics, including patents, and deals with methods and the theory underlying them.   Present issues are divided into the following subjects: Gravitational methods, Magnetic methods, Seismic methods, Electrical methods, Radioactive methods, Geothermal methods, Geochemical methods, Unclassified geophysical subjects, Related non-geophysical subjects, and Patents. "Geophysical Abstracts" 1 to 86 were issued as *U.S. Bureau of Mines Information Circulars;* Nos. 87 to 111 were issued as *U.S. Geological Survey Bulletins,* four to a bulletin; Nos. 112 to 127 were issued as *Bureau of Mines Information Circulars;* beginning with No. 128 the publication is again issued as *Geological Survey Bulletins,* which are sold by the Superintendent of Documents (see page 104).   The equivalent of a subscription to this publication can be obtained by depositing $5 or more with the Superintendent of Documents.   The numbers issued by the Bureau of Mines are all out of print and out of stock.   Each number of "Geophysical Abstracts" has been indexed; each *Geological Survey Bulletin* also contains an index to the several numbers included within it.   The following more comprehensive indexes have been issued.

Numbers	Bureau of Mines Information Circular
1 to 20	6438
21 to 32	6589
112 to 115	7273
116 to 119	7310
124 to 127	7414

The geophysical abstracts in the *Colorado School of Mines Magazine* since Vol. 21, No. 1, January 1931, were preceded by a separate mimeographed publication called *Geophysical News and Review of Geophysical Literature,* which was issued monthly from February 1928 to May 1930 for private circulation by the Geophysics Department of the Colorado School of Mines, Golden, Colorado.   The contents were variously arranged; the total paging was 132.

The Society of Exploration Geophysicists, Tulsa, has published "Patent Abstracts Published in Geophysics by Inventor, Subject and Patent Number," covering the years 1939 to 1947.

Ground water

Abstracts of all the publications of the U.S. Geological Survey and cooperating agencies relating to ground water are given in *Water-Supply Paper* 992 (1947, 412 pp.), sold by the Superintendent of Documents,

Government Printing Office, Washington. Included are 919 publications of the Geological Survey; 276 cooperative reports published by the various states, Hawaii, Antigua, and Haiti; 209 short papers originally processed by the Geological Survey; and 373 articles written by members of the Geological Survey and published in various outside periodicals. It covers through January 1946 and supersedes *Water-Supply Paper* 427, which was issued in 1918.

Mineralogy

The most comprehensive abstract publication in the field of mineralogy is *Mineralogical Abstracts*, edited by Lester J. Spencer, and issued in London as a separately paged appendix to *The Mineralogical Magazine and Journal of the Mineralogical Society*. It covers the literature since 1915, continuing the last volume (1914) published by the *International Catalogue of Scientific Literature* (see page 62). The abstracts are classified according to a number of major subjects which vary in different issues; some frequent ones are notices of books, bibliographies, history and biography, new minerals, artificial minerals, X rays and crystal structure, precious stones, meteorites, rock-forming minerals and petrology, topographical mineralogy, and miscellaneous. The 12 numbers of Vol. 1 (1920 to 1922), issued with Vol. 19 of *The Mineralogical Magazine*, are also sold separately. The later numbers were issued only as part of the periodical; most of the quarterly numbers are still available from the General Secretary of the Mineralogical Society, British Museum of Natural History, South Kensington.

Mining

The Mining World Index of Current Literature was published semiannually from 1912 to 1916 (10 vols.) by the Mining World Company, Chicago. It was "compiled and revised semiannually from the index of the world's current literature appearing weekly in *Mining and Engineering World.*" Covering articles in periodicals, papers read at scientific and technical meetings, bulletins, and books, its brief annotations of all entries gave it the status of an abstract journal. It had four main parts: Geology and mineralogy, Ores and mineral products, Technology, and Miscellaneous. Each part was further divided by subjects into separate chapters.

The English edition of *Technische Auskunft* was published as *Engineering Abstracts* by the International Institute of Technical Bibliography, London. Four volumes were issued from 1910 to 1913. The seven sections were printed annually as separate books, of which No. 4 was "Mining and Metallurgical Abstracts."

Petroleum

Abstracts of articles on the geology and the technology of petroleum and petroleum products have been published and paged separately and indexed annually by author and subject since 1920 (Vol. 7) by the *Journal of the Institute of Petroleum*, London.

Abstracts in petroleum technology appear in *Library Bulletin of Abstracts*, published since 1926 by Universal Oil Products Company, Chicago. It is now issued weekly and has annual author and subject indexes.

Coal

Some abstracts on the geology of coal appear in *Fuel Abstracts*, prepared by Fuel Research Station, London, and published since 1925 by H. M. Stationery Office, London. Prior to 1945 it was called *Fuel Research Intelligence Section Weekly Summary*.

GENERAL SCIENCE AND TECHNOLOGY

Australian Science Abstracts has been published quarterly since 1922 by the Australian National Research Council; since 1938 it has been published as a supplement to the *Australian Journal of Science*. Short abstracts of the publications of Australian scientific workers are arranged by sections according to the branches of science represented on the Council, including Mining and metallurgy, Chemistry, and Engineering. The abstracts are numbered consecutively and continuously; each section is arranged alphabetically by author. There is no index.

Abstracts of all scientific papers published in India, published abroad on work done in India, or based upon Indian material are given in *Indian Science Abstracts*, published since 1935 by the National Institute of Sciences of India, Calcutta.

Chemistry

The chief scientific abstract journal in the world is *Chemical Abstracts*, published since 1907 by the American Chemical Society, Easton, Pennsylvania. The editorial office, however, is at Ohio State University, Columbus, Ohio. It is issued semimonthly on the 10th and 20th. Entries are secured from about 2,800 periodicals and checked for completeness with other abstract journals. The abstracts are classified in 31 groups, of which No. 8, edited by Michael Fleischer, deals with "Mineralogical and Geological Chemistry." The abstracts within each section are arranged in the following order: abstracts of articles, cross references to other sections, books, patents, theses.

An author index is in each issue. An annual author index, subject index, formula index, and numerical patent index are given in the issues for

Dec. 10 and 20; the formula index has appeared since 1920, the patent index appeared from 1912 to 1914 and has been included since 1935. Cumulative author indexes and subject indexes have been published every 10 years since 1917 (1917, 1927, 1937, 1947—A to K); the first of these decennial indexes was reproduced in four volumes in December 1947 by J. W. Edwards, Ann Arbor, Michigan. The index references since January 1934 have been given with the number of the column (two to a' page) and a small exponent which indicates on which ninth of the page the abstract is to be found. The key to the subject index and key to the formula index will aid greatly in using the indexes. The "List of Periodicals Abstracted" catalogues the periodicals alphabetically according to the authorized abbreviations of the International Union of Chemistry and gives also the full title, the frequency of appearance, the 1946 volume number (the first of these if there is more than one per year), the first number of that volume (if other than 1), the number of volumes per year, the price, the publisher's name and address, and numbers designating libraries in the United States, Canada, Hawaii, and Puerto Rico which currently receive the periodical. A list of 280 libraries, their geographic distribution, and their lending, microfilming, photoprinting, and translating services is also given. The probable status is shown for publications whose distribution has been affected by the war. The latest "List of Periodicals Abstracted" is in Vol. 40, No. 24, Pt. 2, of *Chemical Abstracts*, Dec. 20, 1946, 209 pp.

Chemical Abstracts was preceded (before 1907) by the abstracts issued from 1897 to 1906 as part of the *Journal of the American Chemical Society*. This periodical was, in turn, the outgrowth of the *Review of American Chemical Research* issued from April 1895 to December 1901 as a part of the *Technology Quarterly*.

The Bureau of Abstracts, London, publishes *British Abstracts*. The abstracts are divided into three sections. Section A, Pure Chemistry, is issued monthly. There are three chief divisions; the last part of the first division is Geochemistry. Section B, Applied Chemistry, is issued monthly as a supplement to the weekly periodical *Chemistry and Industry;* from 1926 to 1936 it was issued semimonthly as a section of the *Journal of the Society of Chemical Industry* and called *British Chemical Abstracts*. Section C, Analysis and apparatus, began in 1944. None of the sections have many abstracts of books. All sections are covered in the same index. Annual author indexes, subject indexes, and patent indexes are also published. Cumulative author and subject indexes are available for 1923 to 1932 and 1933 to 1937. Corrections are listed in the annual indexes.

Chemisches Zentralblatt is now published weekly under the joint auspices of Deutsche Akademie der Wissenschaften, Berlin, Akademie der Wissenschaften, Goettingen, and Gesellschaft deutschen Chemiker, Berlin. This

title has been in use since 1907; the publication was previously issued as

Pharmaceutisches Centralblatt, 1830 to 1849, 1 vol. per year
Chemisches-Pharmaceutisches Centralblatt, 1850 to 1855, 1 vol. per year
Chemisches Centralblatt, 1856 to 1888, 1 vol. per year
Chemisches Centralblatt, 1889 to 1907, 2 vols. per year
Chemisches Zentralblatt, 1907 to 1919, 2 vols. per year
Abstracts of *Zeitschrift für angewandte Chemie* were added in 1919.
Chemisches Zentralblatt, 1919 to 1924, 4 vols. per year: Vols. 1, 3, Scientific;
    Vols. 2, 4, Technical
Chemisches Zentralblatt, 1924 to date, 2 vols. per year

Most of the wartime volumes (111 to 116, 1940 to 1945) are now available
in facsimile reprint from J. W. Edwards, Ann Arbor, Michigan.

The abstracts are divided into eight main groups, of which Group *C*
is Mineralogy and geology.   The abstracts within each section are arranged
as follows: articles, patents, books (books were listed as a supplement
called *Bibliographia chemica* from 1922 to 1926).   The Vorwort explains
the arrangement.

There is an author index and a book index in each issue.   Semiannual
author indexes and patent indexes are published.   The patent index has
been issued since 1897, and a semiannual subject index was issued from
1889 to 1924 only.   An annual subject index (combined with the author
index until 1925) and organic formula index (since 1925) are issued.   Various cumulative indexes have been published at intervals (1870 to 1881,
1897 to 1901, 1902 to 1906, 1907 to 1911, 1912 to 1916, 1917 to 1921, 1922
to 1924, 1925 to 1929, 1930 to 1934).   Corrections are noted in the annual
and cumulative indexes.

Abstracts in chemistry were published monthly by the Chemical Society,
London, in or with the *Journal of the Chemical Society* from 1871 to 1925.
They were issued with the rest of the periodical from 1871 to 1877 and as a
separate (even-numbered) volume from 1878 to 1925.   The abstracts were
issued in two parts from 1893 to 1925—Part 1: Organic, physiological, and
agricultural chemistry; Part 2: General and physical chemistry.   The
abstracts were issued independently of the periodical from 1924 to 1925 as
"Abstracts of Chemical Papers Issued by the Bureau of Chemical Abstracts."   These abstracts became Section A, Pure Chemistry, when they
were combined in 1926 with the abstracts of the *Journal of the Society of
Chemical Industry* to form *British Chemical Abstracts*.   An author index is
in each issue.   Annual author indexes and subject indexes were issued from
1882 to 1925; the abstracts were indexed with the rest of the periodical
from 1882 to 1890.   Cumulative author indexes and subject indexes are
available for 1873 to 1882, 1883 to 1892, 1893 to 1902, 1903 to 1912, 1913

to 1922. The subject indexes are partly grouped into general headings. Corrections are given in the cumulative indexes.

Chemistry and Industry, formerly called the *Journal of the Society of Chemical Industry*, has been published by the Society of Chemical Industry, London, since 1882. The abstracts were combined with the rest of the periodical from 1882 to 1918 and have appeared as a separate section (Section A) since 1918. The abstracts were issued weekly from 1882 to 1925, semimonthly from 1926 to 1936, and monthly since then. These abstracts became Part B, Applied Chemistry, when they were combined in 1926 with the abstracts of the *Journal of the Chemical Society* to form *British Chemical Abstracts*, but they continue to be regarded as a part of *Chemistry and Industry*. Annual author indexes, subject indexes, and patent indexes are issued. Cumulative author and subject indexes were published for 1883 to 1895, 1896 to 1905. Corrections appear in the annual and cumulative indexes.

General abstracts on pure chemistry were published until 1933 in the *Bulletin de la société chimique de France*, published by the Société chimique de France, Paris. It was called the *Bulletin de la société chimique de Paris* from 1858 to 1906. Abstracts (Travaux) have been issued since 1863; they were published with the Memoirs until 1892. Abstracts of foreign publications were issued separately each year from 1892 to 1920; all abstracts (both French and foreign) have been issued monthly with the rest of the periodical since 1920 but are annually bound separately in even-numbered volumes. The abstracts are indexed with the whole periodical. Annual author and subject indexes have been issued since 1864 (an author index only in 1863). Cumulative author and subject indexes are available for 1858 to 1874, 1875 to 1888, 1889 to 1898, 1899 to 1906, 1907 to 1916, 1917 to 1926.

General abstracts on applied chemistry are published in *Chimie et industrie*, published by the Société de chimie industrielle, Paris. It has been issued monthly since 1918, one volume per year in 1918 and 1919 and two volumes per year since 1919; about half of the periodical consists of abstracts classified decimally. The pages are numbered independently for the volume and for the four divisions (*A, B, C, D*) in each number. There are annual author indexes, subject indexes, book indexes, and patent-number indexes (the patent indexes since 1930). Page references are given to both the volume and the division.

Chemical abstracts of technological interest were included in the *Zeitschrift für angewandte Chemie*, which was published by the Verein Deutscher Chemiker, Berlin. It was issued weekly in one volume from 1888 to 1903 and in one volume of two parts from 1904 to 1912, combined and paged with the rest of the periodical; from 1913 to 1918 it appeared in one volume of three separately paged parts. The abstracts were made a part of *Chemische Zentralblatt* in 1919. Annual author indexes, subject indexes, and patent indexes were issued. Cumulative author indexes, subject indexes, and patent indexes were published for 1887 to 1907 and 1908 to 1927. Corrections were given in the annual indexes.

General chemical abstracts have been published since 1882 in the *Chemiker-Zeitung*. The abstract section has been called the "Chemischtechnische Übersicht" since 1916; before that it was called the "Chemisches Repertorium." The periodical was issued semiweekly from 1882 to 1908 and three times weekly since. About half of the wartime volumes (64 to 69, 1940 to 1945) are now available in facsimile reprint from J. W. Edwards, Ann Arbor, Michigan. Annual author and subject indexes are published, the latter being grouped into 33 sections.

Other current and obsolete periodicals in general chemistry, physical chemistry, and special fields of chemistry and chemical technology have published abstracts as part of their contents. A complete list of such periodicals would be virtually impossible to compile; lists of various lengths have been published in the following places:

M. E. Sparks, "Chemical Literature and Its Use," published privately, Urbana, Ill., p. 34, 1921.

E. J. Crane and Austin M. Patterson, "A Guide to the Literature of Chemistry," pp. 91, 236–238, John Wiley & Sons, Inc., New York, 1927.

Carnegie Library Publications, Pittsburgh, Pa., technical indexes and bibliographies, at intervals.

National Research Council Bulletin, Vol. 1, No. 3, "Periodical Bibliographies and Abstracts for the Scientific and Technological Journals of the World."

Clarence J. West and D. D. Berolzheimer, "Bibliography of Bibliographies on Chemistry and Chemical Technology," *National Research Council Bulletin* 50, p. 12, 1925.

Physics

Abstracts of physics articles in periodicals and bulletins are published in *Science Abstracts*, issued monthly since 1897 by the Institution of Electrical Engineers, London. Since 1903 this abstract serial has been issued in two separate parts: Section A, "Physics Abstracts," and Section B, "Electrical Engineering Abstracts." Section A has entries under Crystallography (including Mineralogy) and Geophysics, classified according to the Universal decimal classification.

Physics abstracts were published in *Der Fortschritte der Physik* from 1845 to 1918, a total of 74 volumes being issued in 141 volumes by the Deutschen physikalischen Gesellschaft and other publishers. The *Beiblätter zu den*

Annalen der Physik published abstracts from 1877 to 1919. These publications were continued by the *Physikalische Berichte*, published since 1920 by the Deutsche physikalische Gesellschaft and the Deutsche Gesellschaft für technische Physik; it abstracts about 250 periodicals and some books and theses.

Engineering

The Engineering Index contains annually 50,000 to 80,000 very brief abstracts to the international technological literature, indexing many hundreds of periodicals and hundreds of the several other types of publications in about 20 languages. It is published by Engineering Index, Inc., Engineering Societies Library, New York. The contents are classified alphabetically by subject in 287 divisions. A separate author index has been added since 1928. Geology and geophysics, scarcely represented in the early volumes, have had increased space during recent years. With the inauguration by Engineering Index, Inc., of its weekly card-index service in January 1928 (see page 27), the cards were incorporated in *The Engineering Index*. It was bound annually in two volumes from 1928 to 1930 and has been incorporated into a single volume annually since 1931. Following is a bibliographic outline of the publication.

Volume	Date	Title	Publisher
1	1884–1891	*Descriptive Index of Current Engineering Literature*	Association of Engineering Societies
2	1892–1895	*The Engineering Index*	Engineering Magazine Company
3	1896–1900	*The Engineering Index*	Engineering Magazine Company
4	1901–1905	*The Engineering Index*	Engineering Magazine Company
Annually	1906–1917	*The Engineering Index Annual for 19...*	Engineering Magazine Company
Annually	1918	*The Engineering Index Annual for 1918*	American Society of Mechanical Engineers
Annually	1919–1933	*The Engineering Index*	American Society of Mechanical Engineers
Annually	1934–	*The Engineering Index*	Engineering Index, Inc.

Engineers' Digest, published monthly by Engineers' Digest Ltd., London, abstracts articles in the non-British press.

The wealth of scientific and technical information available in the reports of the Office of Technical Services of the Department of Commerce,

Washington, has been described on pages 46 and 56. These reports are listed and abstracted in the *Bibliography of Technical Reports*, published monthly.

Theses

Microfilm Abstracts is a semiannual compilation of abstracts of doctoral theses published by University Microfilms, Ann Arbor, Michigan, from which the full text of the theses may be purchased in microfilm. Each issue contains a cumulative index of titles abstracted in preceding issues. Beginning with Vol. 6, No. 2, abstracts of longer monographs have been included besides theses.

Collections of abstracts of theses are listed in "Guide to Bibliography of Theses" by Thomas R. Palfrey and Henry E. Coleman, described in Chap. 17.

CHAPTER 9

PERIODICALS

The publications that are the chief repository of original and current geologic material, issued at more or less regular intervals, are referred to as journals, periodicals, or magazines, though often appearing under a title such as proceedings or transactions or the foreign equivalent. They constitute the main primary source of geologic information. Most, though by no means all, original material in geology is presented first in such periodicals. Even when research makes its ultimate appearance in a bulletin or book, some earlier abbreviation, condensation, or note is apt to be found in a periodical, if only for the purpose of obtaining priority. Though far less well organized than book literature, periodical literature is chiefly significant for its recency, regularity, and detail.

Periodicals are the outgrowth of personal correspondence between scientists and of the assembled minutes or records of scientific meetings. From the time when all aspects of science were covered in a single periodical devoted to general science (beginning in 1665 with *Philosophical Transactions of the Royal Society*), the increase of scientific knowledge led first to independent periodicals for each kind of science (as geology, chemistry, physics), then to separate periodicals for the chief branches of each science (as mineralogy, paleontology, geophysics), and finally to periodicals in increasingly specialized subjects (as crystallography and petrography). All four types of periodicals exist today in geology, from the most general to the most specialized ones.

Because of the interests of their editors or financial backers, some of the earlier periodicals, supposedly devoted to general science, have emphasized geology out of proportion to its actual importance without changing the title of the periodical as this trend developed. Hence the present nature of such periodicals is not always evident from the title. Examples of such periodicals that contain a preponderance of geologic material are the *American Journal of Science* (begun in 1818 as *Silliman's Journal*) and the Russian language *Bulletin de l'académie des sciences de l'Union des Républiques Soviétique Socialistes* (Akademiia nauk S.S.S.R. *Bulletin*), formerly *Bulletin de l'académie des sciences de Russie*, which have been among the important publishers of geologic research.

The articles or individual contributions are often called "papers" in scientific periodicals, just as similar articles in literary publications are, often inexactly, called essays.

Most periodicals are published by professional societies; others are sponsored by educational institutions or public agencies or are published by private persons and companies either as a business enterprise for profit or as a "house organ" for the purpose of institutional advertising. The latter type of publication may often, perhaps with more justification, be regarded as a bulletin, and so it is discussed further in Chap. 11. The periodicals published by commercial firms, either as a direct source of income or as a house organ for indirect profit, emphasize technological, industrial, and economic aspects of the subject, whereas the other types of periodicals lay stress on scientific aspects.

Although the fundamental purpose of periodicals is to furnish a place for the appearance of original articles, most periodicals have a much wider range of content. Typical of the variety of material, some or all of which may be found in a given geologic periodical, are news of societies, announcements of future meetings, reports on past meetings, personal (including biographical and obituary) news, industrial developments and commercial reports, notes on research, abstracts, reviews and reprints of articles in other periodicals or talks at scientific meetings, letters and discussions, book reviews, lists of new literature, and advertisements (sometimes as important as the articles and as interesting). Two of these items are discussed further elsewhere in this book—abstracts in Chap. 8 and book reviews in Chap. 15.

The frequency of periodicals varies generally from weekly to monthly. The promptness with which contributions are published after being received is an important related factor. Page numbering is usually (but not always) consecutive throughout a single volume. Most volumes represent a year's publication, but some of the more frequent or extensive periodicals are issued in more than one volume, and occasionally a publication that is issued infrequently or is small in size covers several years in a single volume, thereby saving in binding and indexing costs.

Four of the five W's of the newspaperman—Who, What, Where, and When—are required for success in investigating references in periodical literature.

Who. The name of the author may be printed in full, or his surname may be printed alone or with one or more initials. Joint authors are usually given equal prominence unless there are three or more. Even then all may be included; otherwise, the first (supposedly the senior) author may be regarded as the editor and his name alone will appear, perhaps with *et al.* or *and others* appended.

What. This question should be answered with reasonable adequacy by the title. At their best, however, titles can never fully substitute for abstracts, and they are seldom at their best—sometimes being journalistic in style, other times being sedately but cryptically worded. The same defect is found even more frequently in indexes, which may make use of all the significant words in a title but of necessity omit an entry to the precise subject for which the reader is searching.

Where. Names of periodicals are not always easy to determine. Some of the older periodicals and some foreign periodicals are commonly or popularly referred to under names which no longer appear on the title pages, having been superseded by other names which nevertheless may not be so widely known and used.

Similarity of names also causes confusion at times, especially when the references are given in a too simplified form. Brevity and abbreviations can be troublesome even when there is no similar name with which to contend; consequently an extensive list of periodicals, giving full names, common abbreviations, and popular names, is a useful tool to the reader. Abbreviations, which were formerly consistent only within a given periodical, are now fairly well standardized, a procedure which began in the chemical field in 1922. The abbreviations standardized by the International Union of Chemistry can be found for current and recently expired periodicals in the "List of Periodicals Abstracted" by *Chemical Abstracts.* The latest list is in Vol. 40, No. 24, Pt. 2, of *Chemical Abstracts,* Dec. 20, 1946, 209 pp. Other names (both current and obsolete) of present and former periodicals, as well as abbreviations, will be found in the lists of periodicals indicated on pages 89 to 96 of this chapter.

When. The time of publication means more than merely the year if complete information is to be recorded. It may be regarded as also including data as to the precise position which the article or particular reference occupies in the long sequence of a periodical. The unit of dating is usually expressed in years. Where the paging in a periodical is independent for each issue, a more specific date (such as the season, month, or day) may be given.

Inasmuch as most scientific periodicals are issued in volumes, each of which generally corresponds to a year (though there are occasional longer and shorter volumes), the volume number is often substituted for the year. Usually both are given, supplementing each other for purposes of convenience; knowledge of the year is often useful in deciding if the age of the article is within the limits desired.

Some periodicals have been issued in series. The numbering of the volumes may begin anew with each series, and both numbers are necessary unless the year is also given. The most troublesome of such periodicals is the *American Journal of Science,* about which the following bibliographic data may be useful.

Se-ries	Year	Vol-ume	Whole number	Frequency	Name
1	1818–1845	1–50	1–50	1818–1825 irregularly 1826–1845 quarterly	1818–1819 *American Journal of Science*
2	1846–1870	1–50	51–100	Bimonthly	1820–1879 *American Journal of Science and Arts*
3	1871–1895	1–50	101–150	Monthly	1880– *American Journal of Science*
4	1896–1920	1–50	151–200	Monthly	
5	1921–	1–	201–	Monthly	

The number of the issue of a periodical is sometimes given, especially when the page numbers are not continuous throughout a volume.

The paging is preferably given as inclusive pages when the entire article is indicated and as a single page when a definite statement is referred to. A single page number, however, may, when present, merely state the page on which an article begins. Paging is sometimes confusing when a single periodical has several groups of pages, each classified differently, in the same issue. Worse confusion results when the periodical is separated for binding and then the parts are relabeled differently. A conspicuous example of this sort is *The Mineralogical Magazine* and its *Mineralogical Abstracts*, which are separately paged.

Many variations are possible in the printing of the above data, both as to order and as to type style. Commonly the complete sequence is author, title, name of periodical, series, volume, number, paging, date. A customary (though not invariable) practice in type style puts the title in quotation marks, the name of the periodical (usually abbreviated) in italics, the series in brackets, the volume in boldface (Roman or preferably Arabic numerals), and the date in parentheses. The issue number may also be put in parentheses when the abbreviation *No.* is omitted. The following is an example.

Stafford C. Happ, "Significance of Pleistocene Deltas in Minisink Valley," *Am. Jour. Sci.* [5] **36** (216) 417–439 (1938).

The foreign-language equivalents of some of the terms used for these bibliographic entries are given in the chart on the following page.

Some annoying omissions in the presentation of reference data are as often due to lack of information on the part of the writer as they are to carelessness. Omissions may be filled in or contradictory statements rectified by looking in a synchronistic table, which gives at least the correlative year and volume for selected lists of periodicals. Such a table is given

English	German	French	Spanish	Italian	Danish	Dutch	Swedish
edition	Auflage Ausgabe	édition tirage	edición tirada	edizione impressione	Oplag Udgave	druk oplaag uitgraf	upplaga
series	Folge Reihe	série	serie	serie	Raekke	reeks	följd
volume	Band	tome volume	tomo volumen	tomo volume	Bind	deel	band volym
part	Teil	partie	parte	parte	Del	gedeelte	del
chapter	Kapitel	chapitre	capítulo	capitolo	Kapitel	hoofdstuk	kapitel

in "Handbook of Chemistry," edited by Norbert Adolph Lange, Handbook Publishers, Inc., Sandusky, Ohio (7th ed., pp. 1820–1823, 1949).

Errors

In books, errors are usually corrected in subsequent printings or later editions, although occasionally an errata page is added to pages that are bound after the corrections were noted, or an errata slip is pasted into copies that are to be sold later. No one reading an early copy of the book can determine the existence of an error or suspect that a correction had later been made unless corrected copies of another date are present in the same library.

Errors in periodicals, however, are often more easily located than those in books, because periodicals run in sequence and later issues containing corrections are likely to be available along with the earlier ones. In addition, the correction will probably be indexed, both in the current number and in the cumulative indexes, which the experienced searcher examines first. Such an index correction should preferably be under the author, subject, and title entries but may be placed under "errors," "corrections," and their foreign equivalents (*Druckfehler, Berichtigungen*, etc.). Typographical errors are usually acknowledged as an editorial correction, which may appear almost anywhere in the periodical. Authors' errors may likewise be printed in various places, but they are generally given more prominence, and they may even bear the same title as the original article or have an abbreviated heading sufficiently similar to call it to the attention of readers interested in that subject.

Indexes

The discussion of indexing in Chap. 5 is as applicable to periodicals as to other forms of geologic literature.

Cumulative indexes, covering a period of years (frequently 5 or multiples of 5), are a great convenience in looking up a number of references. They save the time required to examine the separate (usually annual) indexes. Cumulative indexes may afford the indexer an opportunity to correct, improve, and expand the smaller indexes, but they may also introduce new errors into the compilation. In conducting a complete search through the files of a given periodical, after the cumulative indexes have been studied the annual indexes published subsequent to the latest cumulative index should be examined, and then the current issues of the periodical should be scanned, beginning with the first number after the last issue that was included in the annual index.

Many cumulative indexes are available for geologic periodicals. A few have a scope broader than a single periodical; a recent example of this kind is the "Comprehensive Index of A.A.P.G. Publications, 1917–1943," published in 1947 (603 pp.), in which the majority of the entries, but not all, refer to the *Bulletin of the American Association of Petroleum Geologists.*

A list of published cumulative indexes, giving the volumes and years issued, is given in Part 2 of "Bibliography of Bibliographies on Chemistry and Chemical Technology" by West and Berolzheimer.[1]

A comprehensive catalogue of cumulative indexes, with which may be determined the probable existence of such an index for almost all important periodicals, is "A Check List of Cumulative Indexes to Individual Periodicals in the New York Public Library," compiled by Daniel C. Haskell and published in 1942 by the New York Public Library, New York. A cumulative index is therein defined as "one which indexes three volumes of a file and makes at least a slight attempt at the classification of the periodical's contents, either an arrangement by authors or by subjects." Fewer than three volumes are included when these were the entire file of a periodical. Also included (in the absence of any other index) are a few so-called indexes which consist merely of the consecutive tables of contents of the individual volumes. Typewritten indexes compiled by the library and references to other indexes recorded but not available in the library are also included in the book. For periodicals issued by organizations, the date of founding and incorporation and any changes in name are given.

Separates

Articles bound as pamphlets separately from the rest of the periodical are called reprints, preprints, offprints, or separates. Sometimes they may be purchased from the publisher of the periodical, but usually they

[1] West, Clarence J., and D. D. Berolzheimer, "Bibliography of Bibliographies on Chemistry and Chemical Technology," *Nat. Research Council Bull.* 50, Washington, 1925.

are obtainable only from the author, who has ordered them before publication, perhaps being given some free and buying others for exchange or distribution. A mailing address of the author of a scientific article is usually printed with the article, or it may be obtained from the editor of the periodical. Failing to secure the address in this way, one may be able to find it in the roster of a scientific society (either in a recently published membership list or in the mailing list maintained by the secretary or editor) or in one of the common biographical directories, such as *American Men of Science* and the *Who's Who* volumes for individual countries. In addition to the biographical sources described on pages 25 to 33 of Soule's "Library Guide for the Chemist,"[1] the recent series *Biographical Sources for Foreign Countries*, published by the Library of Congress, Washington, will be of help in locating such information. A file of selected reprints can be a very useful part of a library, often more convenient to use then bulky periodicals; satisfactory ways of classifying, indexing, and maintaining them have been discussed in a number of articles under headings such as "filing reprints" in the general scientific publications such as *Science*.

Foreign periodicals

The Second World War interrupted the publication of foreign scientific periodicals, some temporarily and some permanently, while the stocks of some periodicals, awaiting a favorable opportunity for being distributed, were destroyed. New publications have since been established, as some no doubt would have been anyway in the normal course of events, and some names have been changed; stocks that were left intact are now being made available. Important notes on the publication of European scientific periodicals during and since the war are given in "Scientific Publishing in Continental Europe" by Charles Harvey Brown, *Science*, July 18, 1947, pp. 54–58.

Since Apr. 15, 1947, certain German periodicals, both new and reestablished ones, can be ordered from Stechert-Hafner, New York. Their lists, published in the Apr. 15, 1947, issue of their *Book News*, are rather complete, containing 177 scientific and technical periodicals, but do not include periodical publications of universities and scientific societies, which had probably not resumed publication at that date. Available periodicals of especial geologic interest include *Geologische Rundschau* (*Zeitschrift für allgemeine Geologie*, Stuttgart), beginning with Vol. 35.

A supplementary list of postwar German periodicals, including only a few technical ones, appeared in *Kultur-Archiv*, October–November 1946.

A later list of German scientific periodicals is the 1947–1948 catalogue of

---

[1] Soule, Byron A., "Library Guide for the Chemist," McGraw-Hill Book Company, Inc., New York, 1938.

Schoenhof's Foreign Books, Inc., Cambridge, Massachusetts. Geologic periodicals are given on page 7, but *Geologische Rundschau* is the only one listed. Several geographic periodicals are listed in Catalogue No. C145, issued in 1948.

The Periodical Republication Program begun by the Office of Alien Property but liquidated in October 1945 has been continued and expanded by J. W. Edwards, Ann Arbor, Michigan. The program is being continued by reprinting the remaining issues of the volumes of German periodicals which were in process at the time of liquidation, by reprinting volumes previously offered but not yet printed when the program was taken over by J. W. Edwards, and by offering for subscription all volumes formerly offered by that office. The program is being expanded by offering for subscription volumes for other war years not previously offered. The latest catalogue (July 20, 1949) lists 163 such foreign scientific and technical periodicals published from 1939 to 1945. The geologic periodicals listed include *Geologisches Zentralblatt, Metall und Erz, Neues Jahrbuch für Mineralogie, Geologie und Paläontologie* (both *Referate* and *Monatshefte*), *Oel und Kohle* (formerly *Petroleum* and *Brennstoff-Chemie*), *Zeitschrift für Kristallographie, Mineralogie und Petrographie* (both *Zeitschrift für Kristallographie* and *Mineralogische und petrographische Mitteilungen*), *Zeitschrift für Mineralogie, Geologie und Paläontologie*, and *Zeitschrift für praktische Geologie*.

Wartime volumes of almost 800 foreign periodicals that have been copied on microfilm are obtainable from Microfilms, Inc., Ann Arbor, Michigan, which issues a "List of Foreign Periodicals Available on Microfilm," the latest being No. 7, dated June 1, 1946. Positive microfilm is also sold for any complete year of a given periodical; single numbers or articles are available as paper enlargements. The geologic periodicals listed include *Annales de géographie; Annales des mines; Annales des mines et des carburants; Braunkohle; Geological Bulletin* of the Geological Survey of China; *Palaeontologia Sinica; Geographischer Anzeiger; Bulletin* of the Geological Society of China; *Oel und Kohle* (formerly *Petroleum* and *Brennstoff-Chemie*); *Petermann's geographische Mitteilungen; Revue universelle des mines, de la métallurgie, des travaux publics, des sciences et des arts appliqués à l'industrie; Stein industrie; Sandgrube; Strassenbau Part B; Stein-industrie und Steinstrassenbau; Teer und Bitumen; Zeitschrift für Erdkunde; Zeitschrift für Geophysik; Zeitschrift für Kristallographie, Mineralogie und Petrographie* (both parts, *Zeitschrift für Kristallographie* and *Mineralogische und petrographische Mitteilungen); and Zeitschrift für praktische Geologie.*

1947 Periodica U.S.S.R. is a list of almost 200 Russian scientific periodicals that are available for export and can be obtained from American book importers.

Published lists of periodicals in practically all countries of the world are given in the sources enumerated in "Current National Bibliographies" by Parker Worley, published in *The Library of Congress Quarterly Journal*, beginning with Vol. 6, No. 4, August 1949 (see page 182).

Periodicals issued by domestic (including state) and foreign governments are listed in the *Quarterly Journal of Current Acquisitions*, published since 1943 by the Library of Congress as a supplement to the *Annual Report of the Librarian of Congress*.

LISTS OF PERIODICALS

Considering the complex interrelationships of the fields of science and technology and the incredible number of periodicals devoted to them, it would be impossible, if not absurd, to attempt to prepare a "complete" list of periodicals containing material of some geologic interest. Careful selection would be necessary to choose the periodicals that might be regarded as the most important ones; this might best be done partly on a statistical basis according to the frequency with which references are given in the literature to a certain periodical.

Such a study, already referred to in Chap. 1, was made by P. K. L. Gross and A. O. Woodward,[1] who evaluated the serial literature used by American geologists. They found that, unlike chemistry and physics, in which the *Journal of the American Chemical Society* and, to a lesser extent, the *Physical Review* were virtually adequate, because of their size and scope, as the sole source periodicals in these fields, geology was not at all well served by any single publication. Their tables give the relative frequency with which the various chief periodicals were cited; some other types of publications were also included, especially government documents and organization bulletins, which are discussed in this book in Chaps. 10 and 11. Most of the references were found to be in American and Canadian periodicals; articles on mineralogy and glaciation refer to foreign publications more often than articles on other branches of geology.

The names of periodicals are to be found in the lists and card catalogues of libraries and in the printed sources discussed below. These, as well as lesser sources not mentioned, include books; periodicals; lists of dealers and subscription agents; inventories of the holdings and current purchases of general, special (including scientific and technical), and organization libraries; check lists of periodicals according to country, period, and subject; and lists of periodicals issued by governments. The available printed lists of periodicals vary widely in length. The dates should be noted, and care

[1] Gross, P. K. L., and A. O. Woodward, Serial Literature Used by American Geologists, *Science*, Vol. 73, pp. 660–664, 1931.

should be taken to differentiate current from discontinued periodicals; recently discontinued periodicals fall in an intermediate group because, although the publications no longer continue to be printed, references to them may be of a fairly late date.

Selected lists on geology

Twenty-six of the most important geologic periodicals now published in North America are named, among other types of geologic publications, in the "Directory of Geological Material in North America" by J. V. Howell and A. I. Levorsen, on pages 1323 to 1326 in *Bulletin of the American Association of Petroleum Geologists*, Vol. 30, No. 8, Pt. 2, August 1946. The date of the first issue, name and address of the publisher, frequency, price, and brief descriptive notes are given.

Over 250 periodicals are cited in Vol. 1 of the seventh edition of "Dana's System of Mineralogy," by Charles Palache, Harry Berman, and Clifford Frondel, published in 1944 by John Wiley & Sons, Inc., New York, and are listed on pages 48 to 65 of that volume. These references include original references to practically "all measurements and all observations of importance" and also references to certain special compilations of data. "It is believed that this list will serve as well for subsequent volumes, since most periodicals in which mineralogical papers customarily appear are contained in the list." This catalogue is thoroughly annotated, giving the abbreviation for each periodical, any changes or variations in name, the name and place of the publisher, correlation between volume and date, and the number and dates of indexes.

A list of the technical publications from which the card abstracts of Engineering Index, Inc., are prepared (see pages 27, 79) may be obtained free upon request from Engineering Index, Inc., Engineering Societies Library, New York. The list includes the important technical and scientific periodicals (and other publications) received by the Engineering Societies Library Service; some other periodicals not suitable for indexing are also received, but no complete list of them is available. The frequency of publication, place of publication, and name of the issuing organization are given.

Lists on general science, including geology

All sciences are included in "A World List of Scientific Periodicals Published in the Years 1900–1933," issued by the Oxford University Press, New York (2d ed., 1934, 779 pp.). Over 36,000 scientific periodicals are listed, together with their place of publication and the names of 187 libraries holding them.

An older list of early twentieth-century scientific periodicals was published with the *International Catalogue of Scientific Literature.* A 312-page "List of Journals," giving the abbreviations of the names, was issued in 1903, and a 68-page supplement appeared in 1904.

Periodicals devoted to geology, mineralogy, and mining are indexed separately but included alphabetically among the 8,603 periodicals listed in "A Catalogue of Scientific and Technical Periodicals, 1665–1895," compiled by Henry Carrington Bolton. The second edition, with 1,247 pages, was published in 1897 as *Publication* 1076 by the Smithsonian Institution, Washington. It was also issued in *Smithsonian Miscellaneous Collections*, Vol. 40, 1898. Rather full bibliographic details are given, including any changes in name, the names of editors, and the sequence of series. Chronological tables give the date of publication of each volume of the periodicals, and a library check list indicates the location in selected American libraries of about one-third of the periodicals.

William J. Fox has listed American periodicals that were not included in the above publication in *Bulletin of Bibliography*, Vol. 5, pp. 82–85, 1908.

Special Publication 1 of the Library of Harvard University, published in 1879 by the Harvard University Press, Cambridge, Massachusetts, is a "Catalogue of Scientific Serials of All Countries, Including the Transactions of Learned Societies in the Natural, Physical, and Mathematical Sciences, 1633–1876," by Samuel H. Scudder (358 pp.). It is classified by countries and is indexed by towns, titles, and subjects.

Appendix 6 (pp. 279–342) to "A Guide to the Literature of Chemistry," by E. J. Crane and Austin M. Patterson, published in 1927 by John Wiley & Sons, Inc., New York, lists 1,889 periodicals in chemistry and related subjects, of which 1,263 were appearing at the beginning of 1927 and 626 had ceased publication, some of them many years prior to that year. "For current periodicals [1927] it is believed that the list can safely be regarded as pretty nearly complete; for these it takes in the periodicals of many branches of science, the papers in which are only in part a source of chemical information." The list of discontinued periodicals is less complete and contains strictly chemical publications only. For the "current" periodicals are given the standard abbreviation, frequency, number of volumes per year, 1926 record of volume number, price, and name and address of the publisher. For discontinued periodicals the common abbreviation and the years and place of publication are given.

Elsewhere (pages 46 to 76) in the same book are listed the periodicals current in 1927 that were of the greatest chemical interest, classified according to the 30 subjects or fields used in *Chemical Abstracts* and subdivided according to the country of publication. Section 8 (pages 58 to 59) covers Mineralogical and geological chemistry, listing 10 periodicals in the

United States, the British Empire, and Germany. Brief descriptive notes are given for most of the periodicals.

"Library Guide for the Chemist," by Byron A. Soule, published in 1938 by McGraw-Hill Book Company, Inc., New York, has on pages 37 to 38 a table listing 33 scientific periodicals, with emphasis on chemistry. Data given include the year the periodical was started, its frequency, the number of volumes per year, number of the volume in 1937, approximate number of pages per volume, cost, and frequency with which the indexes appear.

A list of 48 periodicals in general science current in 1940, grouped according to 17 countries of publication, is given on pages 24 to 26 of "Chemical Publications" by Melvin Guy Mellon, in the second edition published in 1940 by McGraw-Hill Book Company, Inc., New York. The approved abbreviation and the date of the first issue are given for each. A list of 50 important general chemical periodicals on pages 27 to 29 is arranged according to the date when they appeared, and it gives the abbreviation most often used, the dates of publication (for discontinued periodicals), and any changes in name. A list of 187 specialized chemical periodicals in the 30 classifications used in *Chemical Abstracts*, with the standard abbreviations, is on pages 29 to 33; Section 8 (p. 30) names 6 important periodicals in mineralogical and geological chemistry.

Chemical periodicals are listed in "A Select Bibliography of Chemistry, 1492–1892," compiled by Henry Carrington Bolton and published by the Smithsonian Institution, Washington. In Sec. 7 (pp. 1068–1158) of *Publication* 850, which is Vol. 36 of the *Smithsonian Miscellaneous Collections*, published in 1893, are listed alphabetically 436 chemical periodicals issued between 1492 and 1892; the customary abbreviations for the names are given in an appendix immediately following (pp. 1159–1164). This list is an excerpt from the first edition of the "Catalogue of Scientific and Technical Periodicals" (described on page 91) by the same author, but it was brought down to 1892 and enlarged by the addition of serials published by scientific societies.

Other chemical periodicals are listed in the following supplements: (1) "A Select Bibliography of Chemistry, 1492–1897, First Supplement," published in 1899 as *Publication* 1170, which is Art. 7 of Vol. 39 of the *Smithsonian Miscellaneous Collections*, and covering (pp. 448–471) the literature to the end of 1897, (2) "A Select Bibliography of Chemistry, 1492–1902, Second Supplement," published in 1904 as *Publication* 1440, which is part of Vol. 44 of the *Smithsonian Miscellaneous Collections;* it covers (pp. 219–229) the years 1898 to 1902.

Scientific periodicals are included among others in "American Learned Journals," by John W. Bowker, published in 1946 as *Bulletin* 37, 1945, by the American Council of Learned Societies; and "Publications of Societies: A Provisional List of the Publications of American Scientific, Literary, and

Other Societies from Their Organization," edited by R. R. Bowker and published in 1899 by *Publishers' Weekly*, New York (181 pp.).

A complete list of German scientific periodicals is given in "Handbuch der deutschen Wissenschaft," described on page 131. An aid in keeping track of German geologic and other scientific periodicals is a list of those published just before the collapse of the Third Reich; it appeared in a supplementary number of *Book News*, issued fall, 1949, by Stechert-Hafner, Inc., New York.

General lists

Price List 36, "Government Periodicals," issued free by the Superintendent of Documents, Government Printing Office, Washington, lists the titles, frequency of publication, and prices (domestic and foreign) of periodicals issued by various agencies of the United States government for which paid subscriptions are taken by the Superintendent of Documents.

Periodicals of various kinds are listed in certain books, named below, several of which are available for consultation in practically all libraries.

"Ulrich's Periodicals Directory," 6th ed., published in 1950 by R. R. Bowker Company, New York, enumerates 10,000 periodicals, listed alphabetically in 140 groups. For each periodical are given the title, subtitle, supplements, date of origin, frequency, price, size, publisher, place of publication, information as to annual and cumulative indexes, and notation as to which indexing and abstracting services it is included in.

An inter-American edition of "Ulrich's Periodicals Directory" was published in 1943 but is out of print.

Faxon's Librarians' Guide, issued free annually by the F. W. Faxon Company, Boston, contains an alphabetical list of 2,000 American and foreign periodicals (mostly of a general or popular nature), giving their frequency; the index, title page, and volume records for the year; the subscription price; and indicating in which of the 13 periodical index guides each is indexed.

N. W. Ayer and Son's Directory of Newspapers and Periodicals 1950 is a list of United States and Canadian publications. Scientific periodicals are listed alphabetically by subject, state, and town in a trade, technical, and class list (pages 1350 to 1432), which is indexed on pages 1433 to 1440. This book is published annually by N. W. Ayer & Son, Inc., Philadelphia. An older list of general periodicals is "A Guide to the Current Periodicals and Serials of the United States and Canada," by Henry Ormal Severance, the fifth edition (432 pp.) of which was published in 1931 by G. Wahr, Ann Arbor, Michigan.

British equivalents of *N. W. Ayer and Son's Directory of Newspapers and Periodicals* are *Newspaper Press Directory and Advertisers' Guide* and *Willing's Press Guide*.

A list of new and discontinued periodicals appears three times a year in the *Bulletin of Bibliography* (see page 66). Information about new periodicals and changes in old ones is given in "Magazine Notes" in the front of *Industrial Arts Index* (see page 96) and in "Notes and Announcements" in the front of *Readers Guide to Periodical Literature* (see page 99). New periodicals are listed in the *Bulletin of the New York Public Library*, published monthly.

Periodicals for which United States copyright has been obtained are listed in Pt. 2 of *Catalog of Copyright Entries*, now issued semiannually by the Library of Congress, Washington. Entries (including newspapers) are arranged alphabetically by title; renewals are given at the end of the primary list. An annual index to titles is given in the fourth number each year.

Published lists of periodicals in practically all countries of the world are given in the sources enumerated in "Current National Bibliographies" by Parker Worley, published in *The Library of Congress Quarterly Journal of Current Acquisitions*, beginning with Vol. 6, No. 4, August 1949 (see page 182).

A list of publications which enumerated the periodicals of 11 foreign countries is given on pages 64 to 68 of "Manual of Serials Work" by J. Harris Gable, published in 1937 by the American Library Association, Chicago.

Deutscher Zeitschriften-Katalog, published by Verlagsbuchhandlung Schulze and Company from 1895 to 1922, was a directory of over 3,200 German periodicals.

Additional periodicals issued by various scientific organizations may be found in the lists of such organizations enumerated in Chap. 11.

Library lists

Libraries generally file the names of their periodicals in their card catalogues, keeping them as a separate group of cards or placing them under "periodicals," "serials," "magazines," or "journals." Other libraries merely list their periodicals on sheets of paper. Periodicals that are received currently are often listed in a visible wall guide.

Certain of the larger libraries throughout the world have published lists of their holdings of periodicals. These lists when prepared by libraries, such as the John Crerar Library in Chicago, that are especially strong in science and technology can be very useful in identifying geologic periodicals. A catalogue of such lists is given in Appendix 4 (pp. 267 to 272) of "A Guide to the Literature of Chemistry" by E. J. Crane and Austin M. Patterson, published in 1927 by John Wiley & Sons, Inc., New York.

A specialized library list of periodicals is "Latin American Periodicals Currently Received in the Library of Congress and in the Library of the Department of Agriculture." It was published in 1944 by the Library of Congress, Washington, as its Latin-American Series No. 8 (Charmion Shelby, editor). It covers "recent years, in no case earlier than 1935, and usually subsequent to 1938," and includes the publications called bulletins in this book. The subject index includes entries under Geology, Geophysics, Geography, Mineralogy, and Mining.

Union lists

Periodicals that are not available in the library in which one is working may often be located through a "union list." This is a catalogue either enumerating the periodicals currently received in specified libraries or indicating the extent of their holdings of any particular periodicals.

The names of almost 5,000 scientific and technical periodicals and the names of 200 libraries holding them are given in the third edition of "Union List of Technical Periodicals in Two Hundred Libraries of the Science-Technology Group of the Special Libraries Association," compiled by Elizabeth Gilbert Bowerman and published (in processed form) in 1947 by the Special Libraries Association, New York (292 pp.).

"A World List of Scientific Periodicals Published in the Years 1900–1933" is a union list covering more than 36,000 periodicals in 187 libraries (see page 90).

"A Catalogue of Scientific and Technical Periodicals, 1665–1895" includes a library check list for about one-third of the 8,603 periodicals covered (see page 91).

The most comprehensive union list of periodicals is "Union List of Serials in Libraries of the United States and Canada," edited by Winifred Gregory and published by the H. W. Wilson Company, New York. The second edition, 1943, indicates the holdings in over 600 libraries of 115,000 to 120,000 publications (of which many, if not most, are periodicals as defined here). This 3,065-page volume was augmented in 1945 by a "Supplement 1941–1943" (1,123 pp.).

Files of periodicals in libraries of the United States and Hawaii are recorded in "Local Indexes in American Libraries," edited by Norma O. Ireland and published in 1945 by the F. W. Faxon Company, Boston. The entries augment by either name or date those in similar lists published prior to 1945 but do not duplicate them.

Union lists of periodicals have been compiled by a number of American and Canadian libraries. Although largely superseded by the more extensive volumes described above, they are useful for local reference purposes. A comprehensive directory of such union lists is "A Bibliography of Union Lists of Serials" by Daniel C. Haskell and Karl Brown, on pages 3053 to 3065 of "Union List of Serials in Libraries of the United States and Canada," edited by Winifred Gregory, the H. W. Wilson Company, New York (2d ed., 1943).

Foreign union lists of periodicals are enumerated on pages 24 to 25 of "Guide to Reference Books, " by Isadore Gilbert Mudge, American Library Association, Chicago (6th ed., 1936).

Lacking adequate current information from such union lists, one can obtain from the publisher of a given periodical the names of the libraries in any area that subscribe to it. Some publishers, commercial firms as well as scientific organizations, issue free price lists of the back numbers that can be purchased.

With few exceptions, desired periodicals can be obtained almost anywhere by interlibrary loan (see page 41); bibliographic centers (page 42) are often expecially valuable in performing this service.

All known American periodicals printed before 1825 are being reproduced for wider distribution by University Microfilms, Ann Arbor, Michigan. Otherwise no single library, it is asserted, has more than 35 per cent of the original total of 550 titles.

Index guides to scientific and technical periodicals

The following publications function solely as index guides to the contents of periodicals. Other important index guides that embrace articles in periodicals are discussed in Chap. 7, which describes indexes that serve as guides to more than one kind of literature, among which periodicals may predominate. Here, however, only indexes to periodicals are included; none of these are devoted exclusively to geology, the nearest being indexes to the literature of mining.

"Index of Mining Engineering Literature," by Walter R. Crane, is a classified list of titles from 18 periodicals. It was published by John Wiley & Sons, Inc., New York, Vol. 1 in 1909 and Vol. 2 in 1912, a total of 1,257 pages.

Industrial Arts Index is an alphabetically arranged subject index to 254 engineering, trade, and business periodicals, mostly American. Its entries deal with science, technology, business, and finance. Publication began with four numbers in 1913. The guide is published monthly, with an annual bound volume in December, by the H. W. Wilson Company, New York. Annual cumulations were issued for the years 1913 to 1917; 2-year cumulations cover the years 1918 to 1919, 1920 to 1921, 1922 to 1923, 1924 to 1925, 1926 to 1927, 1928 to 1929, and 1930 to 1931; annual cumulations have appeared since 1932.

The Subject Index to Periodicals has been published since 1915 (between 1915 and 1919 as *Athenaeum Subject Index*) by The Library Association, London. The arrangement is alphabetical by subject, covering over 580 English and foreign periodicals. It formerly consisted of class lists, Class *J* being Science and technology.

"Galloupe's General Index to Engineering Periodicals" was published in two volumes in Boston from 1888 to 1893, covering 1883 to 1887 and 1888 to 1892, respectively.

Repertorium der technischen Journal-Literatur is a subject index to more than 400 periodicals (not limited to German ones), arranged alphabetically by the German word, followed (in volumes since 1892) by the French and English equivalents. Each volume has a detailed subject index to this subject list, and (since 1897) there are author indexes also. Prior to 1879 this index was called *Repertorium der technischen Literatur;* two volumes (1910 and 1911) were published as *Fortschritte der Technik.* The first volume, which covers the years 1823 to 1853, was published by F. Schubarth (Berlin, 1,049 pp.); the next six volumes, by Bruno Kerl for the periods 1854 to 1868, 1869 to 1873, 1874, 1875, 1876, and 1877; and the annual volumes from 1878 to 1909 by the Kaiserliches Patentamt (German patent office.)

Mineralogy, petrography, crystallography, geology, geography, and paleontology were included in Part 2 of *Bibliographie der deutschen naturwissenschaftlichen Litteratur*, published from 1901 to 1914 in Jena and Berlin by Deutsches Bureau der internationalen Bibliographie in Berlin.

Bibliographie der deutschen Zeitschriftenliteratur is a classified list of articles from over 2,000 German periodicals (largely scientific), arranged by subjects. It forms Part 1 of *Internationale Bibliographie der Zeitschriftenliteratur (International Index to Periodicals, Repertoire bibliographique international des revues)* and has been published since 1896 by Felix Dietrich, Leipzig.

Translation into English of the titles of articles published since 1947 in Soviet scientific journals appears in "A Guide to Russian Scientific Periodical Literature," published by Brookhaven National Laboratory, Upton, New York.[1]

Index guides to general periodicals

Among the most essential reference equipment in any library are the general index guides to periodicals. Some of the geologic and other scientific articles indexed in the more specialized index guides already described are included in these publications, and some of the articles entered only in these publications are as professional and technical in treatment as any other articles published elsewhere, but a large proportion of the articles are of a more general, semitechnical, or popular nature, though nonetheless valuable for many purposes. The best way to list these general index guides seems to be according to the period which they cover, inasmuch as some of them are successors to others previously published.

"An Alphabetical Index to Subjects Treated in the Reviews and Other

[1] *Science*, Vol. 109, p. 578, 1949.

Periodicals," by William Frederick Poole, was published in 1848 by G. P.
Putnam's Sons in New York (154 pp.).   It was succeeded by the following
publication.

"An Index to Periodical Literature," by William Frederick Poole, was
published in 1853 by C. B. Norton in New York; its 521 pages brought the
references down to January 1852 and included many more periodicals.
This was succeeded by the following publication.

"Index to Periodical Literature," by William Frederick Poole, combined
the two preceding publications and vastly expanded them into 1,442 pages,
covering 1802 to 1881.   It was published in 1882 by James R. Osgood and
Company, Boston.   With its five supplements, listed below, it is a subject
(but not author) index to nineteenth century English and American
periodicals, largely of general and popular interest.   It was reprinted by
Houghton Mifflin Company, Boston, Massachusetts, in a revised edition,
in one volume and in parts.   The supplements, published by Houghton
Mifflin Company under the title "Poole's Index to Periodical Literature,"
may be tabulated as follows:

Supplement	Editor	Dates	Published	Pages
First	William F. Poole and William I. Fletcher	1882–1886	1888	483
Second	William I. Fletcher	1887–1891	1893	476
Third	William I. Fletcher and Franklin O. Poole	1892–1896	1897	637
Fourth	William I. Fletcher and Mary Poole	1897–1901	1903	646
Fifth	William I. Fletcher and Mary Poole	1902–1907	1908	714

An abridged edition, edited by William I. Fletcher and Mary Poole, was
also published; Vol. 1 covered 1815 to 1899 and Vol. 2 (Supp. 1) covered
1900 to 1904.   The original publications were reprinted in 1938 by Peter
Smith, New York, as "Poole's Guide to Periodical Literature."   It consists
of six volumes, as follows:

Volume	Date
1	1802 to 1881[1]
2	1882 to 1887
3	1887 to 1892
4	1892 to 1896
5	1897 to 1902
6	1902 to 1906

[1] Two parts—*A* to *J*, *K* to *Z*.

The Poole indexes were continued indirectly by "The Magazine Subject-
Index" (1907, published in 1908) and *Annual Magazine Subject-Index*
(since 1908), published annually by the F. W. Faxon Company, Boston.

This publication now also indexes by subject other periodicals, totaling about 140, most of which are of United States origin but some are British and Canadian. Volume 1 included 44 periodicals from their beginning through 1907. (Since 1909 Part 2 of each volume has been the *Dramatic Index.*)

"Nineteenth Century Readers' Guide: 1890–1899" is a two-volume author and subject index to 51 leading periodicals of the nineteenth century, covering the period 1890 to 1899. The publisher is the H. W. Wilson Company, New York. Some of the periodicals are indexed only to the date when they were added to another of the Wilson indexes.

International Index to Periodicals was begun in 1913 as *Readers' Guide Supplement.* The first volume (1907 to 1915) carries the indexing back to Supplement 5 to "Poole's Index to Periodical Literature." It now indexes 280 periodicals in the United States and abroad. It is issued six times a year. Cumulations are published annually in March; except Vol. 1 (1907 to 1915), approximately 3-year cumulations have been issued (since 1916), the latest (Vol. 10) being April 1943 to March 1946.

The best known of the general periodical index guides is *The Readers' Guide to Periodical Literature*, published since 1900 by the H. W. Wilson Company, New York. It indexes by author and subject the contents of 113 current periodicals. Cumulations are issued annually; they were further cumulated triennially from 1900 to 1904 and have been cumulated biennially since 1919 to 1921, the latest (Vol. 15) being March 1945 to April 1947.

The contents of over 40 Canadian periodicals are indexed by author and subject in *Canadian Periodical Index*, which has been issued annually since 1932, now by the Public Libraries Branch of the Ontario Department of Education, as a cumulation of the quarterly indexes published in *Ontario Library Review.*

General periodical indexes published in non-English countries—Belgium, Danish, Dutch, French, German, Italian, Norwegian, and Russian—are described on pages 9 to 11 of "Guide to Reference Books" by Isadore Gilbert Mudge, American Library Association, Chicago (6th ed., 1936).

To these may be added Part B of *Monthly List of Russian Accessions*, published since April 1948 by the Library of Congress, Washington, which is a list of titles of articles in scientific and other periodicals published in Russian (both within and outside the Soviet Union) since 1947 and currently received by the Library of Congress and cooperating libraries. The periodicals are classified by subjects, including Geology and Geography. English translations of the titles of Russian articles in a selected list of scientific and technical periodicals are given in *Translated Contents Lists of Russian Periodicals*, issued in processed form monthly since June 1949 by the Department of Scientific and Industrial Research, London.

CHAPTER 10

UNITED STATES GOVERNMENT DOCUMENTS

The publications of public agencies properly belong together as "bulletins" and are represented in this and following chapters (Chaps. 10 to 14). Some of the publications are given greater emphasis in other chapters where they are of more immediate concern.

Although the word "bulletin" has a fairly clear meaning to most readers, it is a difficult term to define simply. Its usual significance is that of a paper-bound booklet dealing with a single subject published by an organization or a public agency and issued independently of other publications. More often than not, bulletins are members of a series, but when they are published at regular intervals and constitute part of a volume, though they may never be bound as one, they should be regarded as periodicals (described in Chap. 9), many of which contain the word "bulletin" in their titles. Conversely, bulletins include most of the publications going under the names "reports," "circulars," etc., and their foreign equivalents. The publishers of bulletins may be public agencies (ranging from the major branch of a national government to the petty bureau of a town), educational institutions, associations, or business firms.

Although the publications of public agencies (and, to a lesser degree, those of institutions) include index guides, abstract journals, periodicals, full-fledged books, and practically every other type of publication discussed in this book, the bulletin is the typical form in which geologic and other scientific material appears.

Publications of the United States government, called public documents, are treated first (in this chapter). Bulletins of selected organizations of national scope are discussed next (Chap. 11); some of these organizations are semiofficial institutions. The two chapters that follow deal with bulletins of successively smaller American political subdivisions, states (Chap. 12), counties and cities (Chap. 13). Bulletins of other countries are discussed in Chap. 14.

Not only is the United States government the largest publisher in the world and the Government Printing Office the largest printing establishment, but the publications of the Federal government are of critical significance to the geologist. Few sciences or occupations are as dependent upon the work that has been done by the government and published under its auspices as is geology. Economics and agriculture are scarcely more indebted to this source of information. Geologic publications are counted in at least the service, research, and informational categories according

100

to Merritt's[1] functional analysis of United States government publications and in at least five of the seven general-subject fields as classified by the same writer.[2] Geologic publications represent, of course, only an infinitesimally small percentage of these, but they are essential to the geologist.

The terms "government publication" and "government document" are synonymous. As defined by law[3] a public document is "any publication printed at government expense or published by authority of Congress or any government publication office, or of which an edition has been bought by Congress or any government office for division among members of Congress or distribution to government officials or the public."

Merritt[4] has divided the government into 13 separate "publishers," namely, the Legislative Branch, the Judicial Branch, and the Executive Branch, which includes the nine executive departments and (as a group) the 38 independent offices and establishments. For "processed" publications (also called "near-print" and "fugitive" publications—those reproduced by duplicating methods other than the accepted printing processes—for example, mimeograph, multigraph, planograph, photo-offset, rotaprint, multilith)[5] these various divisions of the government are printers as well as publishers, in the sense that they both sponsor and manufacture the publications. This activity, if not in fact contrary to law, has been subject to vigorous criticism as an attempt to circumvent statutory limitations on funds for printing.

For printed publications, the Government Printing Office is merely the printer and the departments, bureaus, commissions, offices, etc., act as the publishers. An extensive 178-page list of government agencies and their subdivisions which have issued publications is given in Vol. 151 of "A Catalog of Books Represented by Library of Congress Printed Cards," published by Edwards Bros., Inc., Ann Arbor, Michigan. A reprint of this list may be obtained free upon request from the Information and Publications Office, Library of Congress, Washington. "United States Author Headings," compiled by George A. Schwegmann, Jr., which includes the headings adopted by the Library of Congress and appearing in its extensive card catalogue (see page 23), was published in 1936 by the Library of Congress.

[1] Merritt, LeRoy Charles, "The United States Government as Publisher," p. 121, University of Chicago Press, Chicago, 1943.

[2] *Ibid.*, pp. 12–16.

[3] 28 U.S. Stat. 601–24 (1895).

[4] Merritt, *op. cit.*, p. 46.

[5] Superintendent of Documents, *United States Government Publications Monthly Catalog*, April 1940, p. iv, Government Printing Office, Washington, D. C.

Probably all these agencies of the government publish something of interest to the earth sciences and the mineral industries, but the major share of such material is confined to a relatively few agencies, of which the Department of the Interior and several of the independent establishments produce by far the largest amount.

The organization of the government is continually undergoing change. The more that the geologist knows about the setup of a particular agency the more easily he can determine the probability of its being the source of published information of interest to him. This knowledge should include the relationship of the agency to others within the organization framework, its obligations and duties, and its current activities. Special or temporary agencies occasionally publish valuable material under titles that do not adequately indicate the contents; certain Senate or House Documents particularly are of this nature. As an example of the latter, Soule[1] refers to the comprehensive (but now obsolete) description of the *Index to Chemical Literature* contained in so unlikely a place as "Appendix K of House Document Number 1110 by the President's Commission on Economy and Efficiency"!

Information about the creation and organization of each government agency can be found in "Checklist of United States Public Documents 1789–1909" (see page 107). Concise information about new developments in the organization of these agencies is given in current issues of *United States Government Publications, Monthly Catalog* (see page 106).

The following condensed outline of the organization of the government, adapted from "United States Government Organization Manual, 1950–1951" (1950), includes only those agencies which the geologist is most likely to encounter as publishers of geologic material.

Executive Branch
   Department of the Interior
     Geological Survey
     Bureau of Mines
   Department of Agriculture
   Department of Commerce
     Coast and Geodetic Survey
     National Bureau of Standards
   Independent offices and establishments
     Smithsonian Institution
       United States National Museum

The actual distribution of government documents is effected in three

[1] Soule, Byron A., "Library Guide for the Chemist," p. 252, McGraw-Hill Book Company, Inc., New York, 1938.

ways—through the Congress, by the issuing office, and by the Superintendent of Documents.

Members of Congress are not the unlimited suppliers of free government publications that the general public believes them to be. They have limited themselves by law to a relatively very small number of copies of publications, even Congressional ones; special authorizations for printing additional copies are not common. Some departmental publications are available in considerable quantity to members of Congress, from whom they can be obtained without cost; most of this literature, however, is distributed without charge anyway and can be secured from the issuing office without the trouble of appealing to one's Senator or Representative. If the publication is not free, the latter procedure may be thought worth while; in addition, of course, there is always the possibility of obtaining from a member of Congress either a free or sales publication that has already been sold out or otherwise exhausted at the issuing office. Most departmental publications, even the free ones, are not made available to members of Congress, who must therefore refer the inquiry to the issuing office. Sales publications cannot be expected from members of Congress unless they are willing to pay for it at the same price as any other person.

The individual departments and their subdivisions distribute most of their publications without charge upon request from members of Congress or the general public. A few special types of publications, such as certain maps and charts, are sold by the departments, but otherwise practically all sales publications are handled only by the Superintendent of Documents. Processed publications are mailed from the office that issues them, whereas printed publications are required (by the law of 1912[1]) to be mailed by the Superintendent of Documents upon order from the departments, for which he is supposed to carry a stock. (Some departments evade the law by ordering printed publications which they mail themselves.[2])

For the former practice of free distribution is being substituted more and more completely the policy of selling as many publications as possible. When the supply of publications which a department has allotted to itself for free distribution or has been allowed by law is exhausted, further requests are referred, with price quoted, to the Superintendent of Documents. Inasmuch as the policy varies according to the department, some departments have little for free distribution, even of processed publications. If the publication is given without charge, a postal-card request to the issuing office is just as effective in securing the desired material as a letter and is

---

[1] 37 U.S. Stat. 414 (1912).

[2] United States Congress, House of Representatives, *Hearings on the Legislative Establishment Appropriation Bill for 1940*, p. 309, Government Printing Office, Washington, D. C., 1939.

recommended as the easier way. Some departments maintain mailing lists covering specific subjects, and publications on those subjects are sent to all on the list without a special request being necessary. It is suggested that persons who are interested in a particular subject inquire at the proper agency about being placed on a mailing list. The present tendency, however, is toward elimination of such mailing lists, and those which are kept are usually revised at intervals by requiring the return of a statement requesting that the given publication continue to be sent.

Some quasi-governmental organizations, such as the National Academy of Sciences, sell their own publications, and some government agencies, such as the Geological Survey, sell part of their publications. By far the greater part of the government publications for which a charge is made, however, is obtainable only from the Superintendent of Documents, Government Printing Office, Washington. As the sales agent for the Public Printer since 1895, the Superintendent of Documents has nothing for free distribution direct to the public except price lists. With a stock of about 65,000 titles, new ones being added at the rate of about 13,000 yearly, about 18 million items are sold annually and about 80 million are given away through Congress and the departments of the government.

The purchaser of a government publication should secure as much information about it as possible, including the kind of publication, issuing office, author if any, and the number. This number, which is sometimes long and complicated (an example is I 19.25: P 87/2/948/sh.1–6) is assigned by the Superintendent of Documents and printed in the price lists and catalogues. Such information is especially necessary for government publications because of the confusing way in which the same material may be printed in several different forms, such as an annual report, a special report, or a "separate" from another source, any of which may be either bound or unbound. Correspondence will be handled more promptly if requests for information are sent separately from orders.

Remittance must be made in advance of shipment, either by paying at the time of ordering or, if the extent of one's purchases warrants, by depositing $5 or more in an account against which subsequent orders may be charged. Postal notes (up to $10), postal money orders, express orders or checks are recommended; currency may be sent at the sender's risk. Postage stamps, foreign money, and defaced or smooth coins are not acceptable. A convenient way to make occasional small purchases is by ordering special coupons, sold 20 for $1 and good until used; the required number of coupons, one or more, can be enclosed with the order. Most publications are available at 25 per cent discount when 100 or more are purchased at the same time. (Book dealers receive the same discount, but the full sales price must be adhered to.)

Postage is not required for shipment within the United States, including Alaska, Guam, Hawaii, Panama Canal Zone, Puerto Rico, the American part of Samoa, and the Virgin Islands. The following foreign countries are also included within the free-postage provision: Bolivia, Canada, Chile, Colombia, Costa Rica, Cuba, Dominican Republic, Ecuador, El Salvador, Guatemala, Haiti, Republic of Honduras, Mexico, Newfoundland (including Labrador), Nicaragua, Panama, Paraguay, Peru, Uruguay, and Venezuela. An additional amount equal to about one-third of the purchase price is required for shipment to other countries. Remittances from foreign countries should be made by international money order or by draft on an American bank, payable to the Superintendent of Documents.

Price lists describing all currently available publications in subjects of present interest are revised at intervals and issued free upon request. Those of most value to geologists, with the outline of their contents as given by the Printing Office, are the following:

No. 15. Geology.
No. 18. Engineering and Surveying. Leveling, tides, magnetism, triangulation, and earthquakes.
No. 36. Government periodicals, for which subscriptions are taken.
No. 42. Irrigation, Drainage, Water Power. Federal Power Commission, water resources.
No. 46. Agricultural Chemistry and Soils and Fertilizers. Soil surveys, soil erosion, and conservation.
No. 48. Weather, Astronomy, and Meteorology. Climate, floods, aerology.
No. 53. Maps. Maps for sale by Superintendent of Documents.
No. 55. National Museum, Smithsonian Institution, Indians.
No. 58. Mines. Explosives, fuel, gas, gasoline, petroleum, minerals.
No. 60. Territories and Insular Possessions. Alaska, Guam, Hawaii, Puerto Rico, Samoa, and Virgin Islands.
No. 64. Standards of Weight and Measure. Tests of glass, leather, metals, paper.
List of field manuals and technical manuals.

The Superintendent of Documents issues twice a month (between July 11, 1928, and Sept. 30, 1942, it was issued weekly) a 4-page circular now called *Selected United States Government Publications*, listing (alphabetically by subject), describing, and pricing a number of current publications of varying importance, most of which are of general interest but some of which are quite restricted in their appeal. Occasionally a publication appears on geology, and this might be the earliest notice that the average geologist may have of it unless he is on the notification list of the issuing agency or reads about it from a government press release in a newspaper or in some promptly published journal, such as *Science*. Both current issues and a free subscription to this advertising circular can be had by writing to the Superintendent of Documents.

Under the full title *United States Government Publications, Monthly Catalog* is published a complete list of government publications received by the Library of the Division of Public Documents during each calendar month. It is distributed 3 weeks after the month covered. The first number was issued in January 1895; the title has had four other forms. In addition to the publications of Federal agencies, those of government-owned or controlled corporations, of the local government of the District of Columbia, and of certain unofficial organizations such as the Pan-American Union are included. Listed are separate issues of periodicals, reprints, advance sheets, preprints, briefs, transcripts of record, posters, maps, and charts. Occasionally from 1933 to 1936 and consistently since January 1936, as many processed publications have been listed as have been available, including documents published for official use only. Only confidential publications, processed press releases, blank forms, bills and resolutions introduced in Congress, individual drawings and specifications of the Patent Office, and publications of a few special commissions are excluded from the so-called *Monthly Catalog.*

The titles are arranged alphabetically by subject under the agency that issued them. The *Monthly Catalog* lists the documents printed during the preceding month and tells where they can be obtained and at what price. Full titles and pages and useful notes concerning series, reprint editions, and contents are given. Publications distributed to depository libraries are indicated. An alphabetical list of agencies issuing publications is given, as well as a list of new classifications of documents and information about discontinued series. Previews of publications received in page-proof form and preliminary catalogue entries are also included; advance orders will be accepted for these items. An index appears in each issue, and one is published annually for the calendar year; from 1908–1909 to 1933–1934 it covered the period July 1 to June 30. The index contains entries according to subject, author, title (either series or individual title), and issuing agency.

Publications which were missed by the *Monthly Catalog* were formerly caught by the *Document Catalog* until 1940. To provide for these entries three biennial issues of *Supplement to United States Government Publications Monthly Catalog* were published. Covering the years 1941–1942, 1943–1944, and 1945–1946, these list all publications that were received in the Library of the Public Documents Division of the Government Printing Office and that were found not to have been included in any other catalogue published by the Superintendent of Documents. Since April 1947 all items have been catalogued in the *Monthly Catalog* as received and none omitted because received late; hence the *Supplements* have been discontinued.

The predecessor to the *Monthly Catalog* was the unofficial *United States Government Publications, a Monthly Catalogue,* edited by J. H. Hickcox and published in Washington from 1885 to 1894.

Under the full title *Catalog of the Public Documents of the . . . Congress and of all Departments of the Government of the United States for the Period from . . . to . . .,* a complete list of all printed and processed publications issued by all the agencies of the government during each Congress has been published every two years since 1896 (covering 1893 to 1895). It is known as the *Document Catalog* and has been issued both in the Congressional series and separately. It has a dictionary arrangement, with authors, titles, and subjects in a single alphabet. Issuing agencies are treated as authors; titles are transcribed exactly from the publications; pages are given accurately in full detail; explanatory notes as to contents are added when necessary for purposes of indexing. Maps and charts, army and navy regulations, briefs, transcripts of records, and confidential publications (when released from that status) are included.

Under the full title *Index to the Reports and Documents of the . . . Congress, . . . Session, . . . to . . .* was published (both in the Congressional series and separately) a numerical list and schedule of all volumes of Congressional reports and documents issued during each session of Congress, beginning with the 1st Session of the 54th Congress (Dec. 2, 1895) and ending with the 2d Session of the 72d Congress (Mar. 4, 1933). The titles vary; this catalogue is popularly known as the *Document Index* and is also called the *Consolidated Index* from the fact that it was issued in index form. Since the beginning of the 73d Congress (Mar. 4, 1933) it has been superseded by the *Numerical Lists and Schedule of Volumes of the Reports and Documents of the . . . Congress, . . . Session, . . . to . . .,* which formerly was a part of the larger publication. Only a little of geologic interest is included in either of these publications. Numbered Congressional documents and reports are also included in the index to the *Congressional Record* and in the annual index to the *Monthly Catalog*. Prior to the *Consolidated Index* sessional indexes were published for the Congressional set.

The above publications were preceded by the catalogues of government documents enumerated below.

"Checklist of United States Public Documents, 1789–1909." The third edition, revised and enlarged (1,707 pp.) and published in 1911 by the Government Printing Office, is the best. The two earlier editions (1892 and 1895) bear somewhat different titles. Volume 1 contains lists of Congressional and departmental publications: Congressional, to the close of the 60th Congress, and departmental, to the end of 1909. A list of errors in this edition is given in the *Monthly Catalog*, May 1912, pages 720 to 721. Volume 2, an index, was not published, and therefore the following publication, which was issued in 1902 as an intermediate stage between the second and third editions, has not been made obsolete:[1] *Tables of and Annotated Index to the Congressional Series of United States Public Documents*; this series extends from the 15th through the 52d Congress.

"Public Documents of the First Fourteen Congresses, 1789–1817," compiled by Adolphus Washington Greely and published in 1900 by the Government Printing Office. A 64-page supplement was published in 1904. These books include the Congressional series preceding those covered in the "Checklist of United States Public Documents, 1789–1909."

"A Descriptive Catalogue of the Governmental Publications of the United States, September 5, 1774–March 4, 1881," compiled by Benjamin Perley Poore and published in 1885 by the Government Printing Office. The entries are arranged chronologically; a general index is included. This 1,392-page book is known as "Poore's Descriptive Catalogue."

"Comprehensive Index to the Publications of the United States Government, 1881–1893," compiled by John G. Ames and published in 1905 (2d ed.) by the Government Printing Office. These two volumes are known as "Ames' Comprehensive Index." Emphasis is stronger on Congressional than on departmental publications.

Other, less important catalogues and indexes of United States government publications are described in the following authoritative guides to the labyrinth of Federal documents.

Laurence F. Schmeckebier, "Government Publications and Their Use," 2d ed., Brookings Institution, Washington, D. C., 1939, 479 pp.

Anne Morris Boyd and Rae Elizabeth Rips, "United States Government Publications," 3d ed., the H. W. Wilson Company, New York, 1949, 627 pp.

James B. Childs, "Government Document Bibliography in the United States and Elsewhere," 3d ed., Government Printing Office, Washington, D. C., 1942, 78 pp.

Out-of-print publications, which can no longer be obtained free or by purchase from one of the three government sources already described, must be bought from dealers in secondhand books. Those who specialize in government publications are the likeliest source of supply; their lists and

[1] Childs, James B., "Government Document Bibliography in the United States and Elsewhere," 3d ed., pp. viii, 1, Government Printing Office, Washington, D. C., 1942.

advertisements may be found in technical and scientific periodicals, periodicals devoted to the library profession and bookselling business, and directories of the book trade, which can be consulted in most libraries.

Government documents can be consulted, with a greater or lesser degree of success, in public, institutional, and private libraries (see Chap. 6). The size and scope of the library determine the availability of publications dealing with geology, which are usually not so widely distributed as are government publications of equal importance in such fields as agricultural practice, business statistics, or sociology, which have a broader appeal.

The largest selection of government publications is usually found in the so-called "depository libraries" named by Congress to receive all government documents printed in Washington. There were in June 1947 a total of 552 depository libraries under the following specifications:

All state libraries
All Territorial libraries
1 library for each Congressional district to be designated by the Representative from that district
1 library to be designated in any part of the state by each Senator
1 library to be designated by each delegate in Congress in any part of a Territory
The libraries of 8 of the executive departments in Washington
The libraries of the United States Military and Naval Academies
The libraries of the land-grant colleges
Alaska Historical Society and Museum Library, Juneau, Alaska
American Antiquarian Society Library, Worcester, Mass.
The library of the Philippine government

The fact that depositories are accredited to certain districts as designations of Representatives who represent other districts is explained by the reapportionment at each decennial census, which changes the geographical position of the Congressional districts. Not all the authorized depository libraries listed above have thus far been designated.

Since Mar. 20, 1922[1] the depository libraries have been required to select the classes of publications which they are qualified to house and care for. In June 1947 a total of 427 libraries took advantage of this choice to secure only part of the vast number of government documents. Consequently, not all geologic material issued since that date can be found in each of these libraries, but only in those designated as geological depositories (no separate list is available) and in the other 126 libraries that receive all the documents.

[1] 42 U.S. Stat. 436 (1922).

The geologic publications received by geological depositories are issued by the U.S. Geological Survey and are grouped by the Superintendent of Documents into the following classifications.

No. 621 Annual Reports....................................I 19.1:

No. 622 Bulletins..I 19.3:

These include papers on geologic structure and mineral resources of the states; annual summaries of mineral resources of Alaska; geophysical abstracts; and a series entitled "Contributions to Economic Geology."

No. 623 General Publications..............................I 19.2:

These include unnumbered publications of a miscellaneous nature.

No. 624 List of Publications Issued (monthly)..............I 19.14[4]:

No. 625 List of Publications of the Geological Survey, not including topographic maps..I 19.14[1]:

No. 626 Professional Papers..............................I 19.16:

These include one subseries, "Shorter Contributions to General Geology," also miscellaneous scientific papers on physiography, petrography, mineralogy, paleontology, economic geology, etc.

No. 627 Water-Supply Papers.............................I 19.13:

A large part of this series is made up of two subseries, namely, "Contributions to Hydrology of the United States" and "Surface Water Supply of the United States," the latter covering different geographic sections; it also includes occasional miscellaneous papers on surface or underground water supplies of certain localities.

Since 1939[1] depository libraries that request them have been able to secure maps published separately, documents published outside Washington, and processed publications (otherwise no processed publications are issued).

Because funds for printing are limited by law, in some cases even decreasing while funds for research were increasing, many scientific and research agencies have been publishing the results of their work in nongovernmental periodicals.

Lists of the Federal agencies that were involved in the economic mobilization of the mineral industry during both world wars are given in the extensive organization charts in "The Domestic Mining Industry of the United States in World War II" by John Davis Morgan, Jr., published by the National Security Resources Board, Washington, 1949. This processed 500-page book is of value in finding obscure geologic literature of past and possibly future military importance.

The following agencies of the Federal government are those which publish the most important geologic literature.

[1] 32 U.S. Stat. 1206 (1938).

DEPARTMENT OF THE INTERIOR

Geological Survey

The U. S. Geological Survey was created by an Act of Congress approved Mar. 3, 1879, in which the director was given the duties of classifying the public lands and examining the geological structure, mineral resources, and products of the national domain. At the time of its establishment the Geological Survey took over certain functions and records of earlier surveys of western areas that had operated in the Interior Department and in the office of the Chief of Engineers of the War Department. There are now five branches: administrative, geological, topographic, conservation, and water resources. District offices are maintained in numerous cities throughout the United States. To disseminate the knowledge that it obtains the Geological Survey issues numerous publications of great value to the geologist. These may be named under the following headings.

Bulletins. These are publications of a fairly specialized nature, including numerous mineralogical and chemical contributions, compilations of reference data, and geologic studies of important areas. The first was issued in 1883, and there was a total of 966 to the beginning of 1950. Some parts of chapters are obtainable separately, as indicated in the price list "Publications of the Geological Survey." Prior to 1933 the chapters published separately were combined in a consolidated volume, but the plan of issuing a consolidated volume for each of the series published first in chapters was abandoned in that year.

Professional Papers. These are important geologic publications, more extensive than the bulletins. The first was issued in 1902, and there was a total of 221 to the beginning of 1950. Some parts or chapters are available separately, as indicated in the price list "Publications of the Geological Survey"; the plan of issuing a consolidated volume for each of the series published first in chapters was abandoned in 1933.

Monographs. These are comprehensive publications, more extensive than the *Professional Papers.* The first was issued in 1890, and a total of 55 were published to the beginning of 1950.

Water-Supply Papers. These are publications dealing with water supplies and their use, including surface water, ground water, and power resources. The first was issued in 1896, and there was a total of 1,080 to the beginning of 1950. Some parts or chapters are available separately, as indicated in the price list "Publications of the Geological Survey"; the plan of issuing a consolidated volume for each of the series published first in chapters was abandoned in 1933.

Administrative publications. These are prepared for use in the Geological Survey but are sold by the Superintendent of Documents. They include formulas, tables, and instructions for the preparation of manuscripts, publications, and maps. The first was issued in 1922, and there was a total of seven to the beginning of 1950, four of them still being in print in 1950.

Circulars. These are reports of a geologic nature, similar to many of the bulletins, but they are all mimeographed. They are free on application from the director, Geological Survey, Washington. The first was issued in 1933, and there was a total of 65 to the beginning of 1950.

Special Publications. These include a list of map symbols, a rock-color chart, a bibliography on coal, and three printed publications and two map publications dealing with Alaska at the time of the gold rush and dated 1898 to 1901 but out of print. Two lists of press releases, preliminary maps, and preliminary reports released by the Geologic Branch and Alaskan Branch from 1938 to 1946 are still available.

Mineral resources. The annual volumes of *Mineral Resources of the United States* published by the Geological Survey for the years 1882 to 1923 contain statistics of production by calendar years and matter relating to technology and resources. Each of the chapters dealing with a particular mineral or group of minerals was usually published separately. In the price list "Publications of the Geological Survey" are indicated the chapters that contain material of special or permanent interest; those containing matter that is mainly statistical, such as makes up the greater part of the volumes, are not noted. *Mineral Resources of the United States* was issued as a separate publication of the Geological Survey for the years 1882 to 1893; it was incorporated in the director's annual report for the years 1894 to 1899; it was again made a separate publication for the years 1900 to 1923. Upon transfer of the Mineral Resources Division of the Geological Survey from the Department of the Interior to the Department of Commerce on July 1, 1925, the volumes covering 1924 and subsequent years were published by the Bureau of Mines (see page 116).

Regulations. These are regulations governing oil and gas operations, coal mining, and other mining methods on public lands. They are prepared for use in the Geological Survey and are distributed free by the director or sold by the Superintendent of Documents. The first one was issued in 1927, and there were a total of three to the beginning of 1950.

Annual Reports. These are reviews of each year's activities and publications. The *First Annual Report of the United States Geological Survey* was issued in 1880. A pocket in the cover of Part 2 of the *Fourteenth Annual Report of the United States Geological Survey* (published in 1894) carries a reconnaissance map of the United States showing the distribution of the geologic systems as far as known in 1893. Parts of the *Sixteenth* to the *Twenty-first Annual Report* form a direct continuation of the separate series *Mineral Resources of the United States*. Until 1902 (beginning with the *Twenty-third Annual Report of the Director of the Geological Survey*, published in 1902 as one volume), these annual reports contained the geologic publications that were henceforth published separately as *Professional Papers*, *Bulletins*, and *Water-Supply Papers*. Annual reports of the director of the Geological Survey for the fiscal years 1933, 1934, and 1935 were not published separately, but a condensed report was included in the annual report of the Secretary of the Interior. For the fiscal years 1936 to date, a limited number of copies of the report as it appeared in the annual report of the Secretary of the Interior were reprinted separately for official use; copies of these reports may be had free upon application from the director, Geological Survey, Washington. Exact titles and paging of each of these annual reports are given in the price list "Publications of the Geological Survey."

Chapter 19 of this book discusses maps separately, including maps accompanied by descriptive texts. Those issued by the U.S. Geological Survey include Folios of the Geologic Atlas of the United States, Geologic Quadrangle Maps of the United States, topographic folios, topographic maps, geologic maps, land-classification maps, base maps, and other maps. Some of them are accompanied by descriptive text material. These folios and maps can be purchased and indexes to them obtained free from the Chief of Distribution, Geological Survey, Washington. Since 1949, maps of areas west of the Mississippi River are also sold and distributed by the Distribution Section, Geological Survey, Federal Center, Denver.

Price List No. 15, which can be obtained free from the Superintendent of Documents, is a catalogue of the printed publications of the Geological Survey that are currently for sale by the Superintendent of Documents.

A complete descriptive list, with extensive subject, area, state, and author indexes ("finding lists") of all book publications and maps (except ordinary topographic maps) of the Geological Survey (out-of-print publications are indicated by an asterisk) are contained in the catalogue "Publications of the Geological Survey," which may be obtained free. This pamphlet is issued at intervals, the most recent list (containing 332 pages) being May 1948. This edition will not be fully revised for about 5 years, but supplements are issued annually. A monthly list of new publications is issued free.

Lists called "Geologic and Other Reports," listing the publications both for sale and out of print in each type of classification (including maps), are available for any state, free upon request.

Information concerning the policies and programs of the Geological Survey may be obtained by addressing the director, U. S. Geological Survey,

Washington.   Map distribution offices, where files of reports and maps are maintained for consultation by the public, are located at the following addresses:

1210 General Services Building, Washington, D.C.
230 New Customhouse, Denver, Colo.
504 Federal Building, Salt Lake City, Utah
234 Federal Building, Tulsa, Okla.

Questions about local water resources and mineral or geologic problems may be submitted to the regional or field office of the appropriate branch nearest the area concerned.

A unique and useful guide to the publications of the Geological Survey (to 1931) is the book "Geologic Index of the Publications of the United States Geological Survey," by George H. Albertson, published in 1931 by Geological Publishing Company, Denver (420 pp.; Supplement, 1932, 15 pp.).   It is a systematic geographic scheme of location, grouping all publications on the United States and Alaska according to latitude and longitude in 30-minute quadrangles and indicating the type of publication, whether annual report, monograph, professional paper, bulletin, water-supply paper, geologic folio, or topographic sheet.

Bureau of Mines

The Bureau of Mines was established by Act of Congress on May 16, 1910, its purposes being to conduct inquiries and scientific and technologic investigations concerning mining and the preparation, treatment, and utilization of mineral substances; to promote health and safety in the mineral industries; to conserve mineral resources and prevent their waste; to further economical development; to increase efficiency in the mining, metallurgical, quarrying, and other mineral industries; and to inquire into the economic conditions affecting these industries.

The Bureau was established in 1910 in the Department of the Interior; in 1925 it was transferred to the Department of Commerce; in 1934 it was returned to the Department of the Interior.   The organization, as provided for in 1949, is shown in the following list.

Director
    Assistant Director
    Assistant to the Director
    Chief Counsel
    Chief Metallurgist
    Chief Mining Engineer
    Chief Economist
    Office of Mineral Reports
    Office of Air and Stream Pollution Research

Minerals Division
  Nonferrous Metals Branch
  Ferrous Branch
  Light Metals
  Rare and Precious Metals
  Fertilizer and Chemicals
  Construction Minerals
Fuels and Explosives Division
  Office of Synthetic Fuels
  Petroleum Branch
  Coal Branch
  Helium Branch
  Explosives Branch
  Coal Economics
  Petroleum Economics
Health and Safety Division
  Coal Mine Inspection Branch
  Safety Branch
  Accident Analysis
  Health
Administrative Division
Regions I to IX

Region	Headquarters
I Alaska	Juneau, Alaska
II Northwest	Albany, Ore.
III Southwestern	San Francisco, Calif.
IV Rocky Mountains	Denver, Colo.
V North Central	Minneapolis, Minn.
VI South Central	Amarillo, Tex.
VII Southeast	Norris, Tenn.
VIII Northeastern	Pittsburgh, Pa.
IX Foreign Minerals	

The Mineral Resources Division of the Geological Survey and the Coal Division of the Bureau of Foreign and Domestic Commerce were transferred to the Bureau of Mines in 1925.

Activities of the Bureau are administered from Washington but are carried on largely in the field offices, laboratories, experiment stations, and pilot plants; a complete directory is given in the latest issue of *Official Organization Handbook—United States Department of the Interior—For Use in 19...* Limited supplies of publications on specific subjects are sometimes available at the office or source of origin in the field. *Coal Mine Inspection Reports* are available for examination at the appropriate district and subdistrict offices in the vicinity of the particular mine.

The organic act of the Bureau, as amended by Congress and approved Feb. 25, 1913, made it the province and duty of the Bureau to "disseminate information concerning these subjects in such manner as will best carry out the purposes of this Act." In accordance with the law, the Bureau issues various types of publications to report the results of its inquiries, studies, and investigations.

In general, there are two classes of Bureau documents: those which are considered to be of enduring or permanent value and are therefore printed and those which are of transitory importance or of less enduring value and are therefore processed by various duplicating methods. Printed publications are usually sold by the Superintendent of Documents, and processed publications are distributed free upon request by the Publications Distribution Section, U.S. Bureau of Mines, Pittsburgh.

The publications of the Bureau of Mines come under the following headings.

Bulletins. Issued at irregular intervals, these describe major investigations conducted by the Bureau and are considered to have permanent value. Usually a bulletin describes research that has been completed, but sometimes one is issued on completion of a significant part of the research. A total of 491 have been published to the beginning of 1951.

Technical Papers. These are preliminary reports on major research projects and progress reports on continuing investigations. A total of 726 have been issued to the beginning of 1951.

Information Circulars. These are popular discussions of material of current interest, written in semitechnical language and designed to provide replies to the types of inquiries received most often by the Bureau. They furnish in processed form compilations, reviews, abstracts, and (mainly) discussions of virtually all activities and developments in the mineral industries. A total of 7,578 have been issued to the beginning of 1951.

Reports of Investigations. These processed reports describe the principal features and results of minor investigations or phases of major investigations, thus keeping the mineral industries and the public advised on the current progress of original research. A total of 4,720 have been issued to the beginning of 1951.

Handbooks. These are manuals, written in simple, nontechnical language, designed largely for use in courses in safety instruction and mine rescue or for guidance in efficient utilization of solid fuels.

Minerals Yearbooks. These annual publications review the mineral industries in the United States and foreign countries during the calendar year covered, giving official statistics on metals, minerals, and mineral products and presenting a factual record of economic and technological developments and trends. Separate chapters ("preprints") may often be purchased independently. Prior to 1924 the annual volumes were published by the U.S. Geological Survey under the title *Mineral Resources of the United States* (see page 112).

Economic Papers. These provide authoritative summaries and analyses regarding production, occurrence, uses, and other essential facts for important minerals in the United States and foreign countries.

Mineral Trade Notes. These processed publications consist largely of abstracts of consular reports and other special reports. During the Second World War they were issued only as a confidential series.

Periodical Reports. These are issued weekly, monthly, quarterly, or annually and contain statistical and economic data for some important mineral commodities, including petroleum products, crude petroleum, coke, anthracite, and cement.

California *Petroleum Statements* are obtainable only from the Petroleum Economics Division, U.S. Bureau of Mines, 1545 Post Office and Courthouse Building, Los Angeles 12, California. All other *Periodical Reports* are obtainable from the Office of Mineral Reports, Bureau of Mines, Washington, D.C.

Arrangements can be made to forward copies of certain *Periodical Reports* regularly as issued if an application stating in detail the need for them is made to the Publications Distribution Section, U.S. Bureau of Mines, Pittsburgh, Pennsylvania.

Mineral Market Reports. These annual processed reports contain information on the production, consumption, and markets of certain mineral commodities for the preceding year and information on the output of gold, silver, copper, lead, and zinc in various states. They are issued as soon after the end of the year as the data are available.

Engineering Reports. These describe conditions and work done at certain oil fields in the United States. They were mimeographed and are now out of print.

Schedules. These describe the procedures and methods followed by the Bureau in testing materials and equipment to determine their permissibility for use by the mineral industries.

Miners' Circulars. These are safety publications prepared primarily for miners but also useful to supervisors. They describe methods of preventing accidents, safe use of equipment and material, first-aid and mine rescue procedures, protective measures against mine gases, and prevention of disease. A total of 61 have been published to the beginning of 1951.

Injury Statistics. Called *Accident Statistics* prior to 1946, these are issued at various intervals, giving summary figures by states for fatal and nonfatal injuries and man-hours worked in mineral industries.

Data Books. These publications are analyses of coal from the districts established under the Bituminous Coal Act of 1937. Prior to 1945 they were issued by the Bituminous Coal Consumers' Counsel in collaboration with the Bureau of Mines. A total of seven have been published to the beginning of 1951.

Monographs. These belong to a series of technical publications, totaling eight, mostly printed under private auspices and available largely from outside sources.

Cooperative publications describing work conducted cooperatively with state departments of geology or mines, colleges and universities, industries, and other organizations are issued by the cooperating agency rather than by the Bureau of Mines itself. The Bureau, however, may issue reports on these publications; they are listed in the catalogues issued free by the Bureau (see below). *Data Books* 1 to 5 (1941–1942), though published in collaboration with the Bituminous Coal Consumers' Counsel, are sold by the Superintendent of Documents.

Daily Press Memos. A considerable backlog of scientific papers and reports, totaling 541, withheld for various reasons during the Second World War, was released for publication during the fiscal year ending June 30, 1946.

Annual Reports. The director of the Bureau describes to the Secretary of the Interior the progress made by the Bureau in all its phases of activity during each fiscal year ending June 30, including information and statistics on the publications enumerated above. Although these are printed, they may be obtained free from the Publications Distribution Section, Bureau of Mines, Washington.

Articles written by members of the staff of the Bureau of Mines and published in outside periodicals and bulletins are listed alphabetically by author and indexed by author and subject in *Bureau of Mines Papers Published in the Technical Press*, obtainable free from the Publications Distribution Section, Bureau of Mines, Washington. The latest issue covers the years 1938 to 1945; the previous ones covered 1934 to 1937, 1931 to 1934, and July 1, 1910, to Dec. 31, 1930.

A catalogue of the printed publications of the Bureau of Mines that are currently for sale by the Superintendent of Documents is contained in Price List No. 58, which can be obtained free from the Superintendent of Documents.

Complete listings, with subject and author indexes (except in the monthly list) of all Bureau of Mines publications, both printed and processed, are contained in the following catalogues, which can be obtained free from the Publications Distribution Section, Bureau of Mines, Washington. Sales and free publications are listed separately.

"List of Publications." 1910 to 1948.
"New Publications: Monthly List."

DEPARTMENT OF AGRICULTURE

The Department of Agriculture publishes material on the geology and sedimentology of soils, in series known as *Circulars, Department Bulletins,*

Farmers' Bulletins, Leaflets, Technical Bulletins, Yearbooks and *Yearbook Separates, Miscellaneous Publications,* and certain unnumbered publications not in a series.

Most of these publications are obtainable free from the Division of Publications, Office of Information, U.S. Department of Agriculture, Washington. They may also be secured from the seven Regional Offices of Information of the Soil Conservation Service, the addresses of which are as follows:

Northeastern Region 1. Center Building, Upper Darby, Pa.
Southeastern Region 2. Spartanburg, S. C.
Upper Mississippi Region 3. 4650 North Port Washington Road, Milwaukee 12, Wis.
Western Gulf Region 4. P.O. Box 1898, Fort Worth 1, Tex.
Northern Great Plains Region 5. P.O. Box 713, Lincoln 1, Neb.
Southwestern Region 6. P.O. Box 1348, Albuquerque, N. M.
Pacific Region 7. Pacific Building, Portland 7, Ore.

Publications which are for sale only are obtainable from the Superintendent of Documents.

All current sales and free publications (as well as charts, posters, photographs, maps, and other visual aids) issued by the Department of Agriculture are listed by subject and issuing office in a 184-page indexed "List of Available Publications," compiled by Eleanor W. Clay of the Division of Publications, Office of Information, and issued as *Miscellaneous Publication* 60, dated November 1929 and revised to November 1948. Price List No. 46 of the Superintendent of Documents lists publications on soil surveys, soil erosion, and related subjects that are currently for sale by the Superintendent of Documents. A *Monthly List of Publications and Motion Pictures* is issued free.

Complete lists of the former publications of the Department of Agriculture are contained in the following publications:

Date	Title
1840 to June 1901	Division of Publications, *Bulletin* 6
1862 to 1902	Bibliography of United States Public Documents, *Department List* 1. Issued in 1904 by the Superintendent of Documents; out of print
1901 to 1925	*Miscellaneous Publication* 9
1926 to 1930	*Miscellaneous Publication* 153
1931 to 1935	*Miscellaneous Publication* 252
1936 to 1940	*Miscellaneous Publication* 443
1941 to 1945	*Miscellaneous Publication* 611

Indexes to the publications of the Department of Agriculture have been issued as unnumbered publications covering the following years: 1901 to 1925, 1926 to 1930, 1931 to 1935, 1936 to 1940. These are sold by the

Superintendent of Documents. Separate indexes to *Department Bulletins, Technical Bulletins,* and *Farmers' Bulletins* are available free upon request from the Division of Publications, Office of Information, U.S. Department of Agriculture, Washington.

DEPARTMENT OF COMMERCE

Coast and Geodetic Survey

Established in 1807 as the Coast Survey, with its chief responsibility that of surveying and charting the coast, the Coast and Geodetic Survey (named in 1878) makes hydrographic and topographic surveys of the coasts of the United States and its territories and possessions, of rivers to the head of ship navigation or tidewater, and of the interior for determination of altitudes and geological positions to furnish control points for surveys; makes observations and does research in gravity and terrestrial magnetic tides and currents; and investigates earthquakes (an activity conducted prior to 1925 by the Weather Bureau).

Publications of the Survey include manuals, reports, maps, charts, and tables. They are issued in order to make available for public use data obtained from the various classes of field surveys made by the Bureau, to provide manuals of instruction for the use of the field force of the Bureau in making field surveys, and to report accomplishments of the Bureau. The subjects covered in these publications are listed alphabetically below.

    Administration
    Astronomy
    Cartography
    Charts and maps
    Coast pilots
    Geodesy
    Geomagnetism
    Gravity
    Hydrography
    Leveling
    Oceanography
    Seismology
    Tides and currents
    Topography
    Triangulation and traverse

Some of these publications are discussed further in Chap. 19 on Maps.

A "List of Publications of the Coast and Geodetic Survey," which lists available publications and indicates from which of the several sources they can be obtained, can be secured free. The third edition is dated

April 1950. The Coast and Geodetic Survey also maintains a mailing list of those interested in receiving notices of new publications in any of the following subjects, for which a request should be made to the director.

No. 109.   Astronomical work
No. 109-*A*.   Base lines
No. 109-*B*.   Coast pilots
No. 109-*C*.   Currents
No. 109-*D*.   Geodesy
No. 109-*E*.   Gravity
No. 109-*F*.   Hydrography
No. 109-*G*.   Leveling
No. 109-*H*.   Nautical charts
No. 109-*I*.   Oceanography
No. 109-*J*.   Traverse
No. 109-*K*.   Seismology
No. 109-*L*.   Terrestrial magnetism
No. 109-*M*.   Tides
No. 109-*N*.   Topography
No. 109-*O*.   Triangulation
No. 109-*P*.   Cartography
No. 109-*R*.   Aeronautical charts

Some Coast and Geodetic Survey publications, particularly nautical charts and related publications, are sold at regular prices in some bookstores, all of which are in coastal towns; a list of such sales agents may be obtained free from the director.

Most publications for which a charge is made are sold by the Superintendent of Documents and by the director, Coast and Geodetic Survey, Washington. Certain publications can be purchased only from the Superintendent of Documents. Many of the publications are also available at 8 of the 10 district offices, the addresses of which follow.

Northeastern District, 10th floor, Customhouse, State Street, Boston 9, Mass.
Eastern District, 602 Federal Office Building, 90 Church Street, New York 7, N. Y.
Southeastern District, 418 Post Office Building, Norfolk 10, Va.
Southern District, 314 Customhouse, 423 Canal Street, New Orleans 16, La.
Southwestern District, 1434 Federal Building, Los Angeles 12, Calif.
Western District, 114 Customhouse, San Francisco 26, Calif.
Mid-Western District, 502 Panama Building, 534 South West Third Avenue, Portland 4, Ore.
Northwestern District, 705 Federal Office Building, Seattle 4, Wash.

The earlier publications of the Survey, from 1816 to 1908, are enumerated in "List and Catalogue of the Publications Issued by the United States

Coast and Geodetic Survey, 1816–1902," which was reprinted in 1908 with a supplement covering the years 1903 to 1908.

National Bureau of Standards

The National Bureau of Standards was established in 1901 to develop, construct, and house reference and working standards used in science, industry, and commerce. Thirteen divisions conduct the principal fundamental research of the Federal government in physics, chemistry, and engineering: Electricity, Metrology, Heat and power, Optics, Chemistry, Mechanics and sound, Organic and fibrous materials, Metallurgy, Mineral products, Simplified practice, Trade standards, Code and specifications, and Ordnance development.

The publications of the Bureau, which are issued as separate series, appear under the following headings:

Class *S*. Scientific Papers
Class *T*. Technologic Papers
Class *C*. Circulars
Class *H*. Handbooks
Class *R*. Simplified Practice Regulations
Class *M*. Miscellaneous Publications

Publications of the Bureau that are currently for sale by the Superintendent of Documents are listed in Price List No. 64, revised at intervals and issued free.

All the publications of the Bureau of Standards from 1901 to June 30, 1947, are listed in *Circular* 460, issued in 1949. Brief abstracts are given for the publications from Jan. 1, 1942, to June 30, 1947.

Technical News Bulletin is a monthly announcement of new publications.

INDEPENDENT OFFICES AND ESTABLISHMENTS

Smithsonian Institution

Created in 1846 by Congress under the terms of the will of James Smithson "for the increase and diffusion of knowledge among men" the Smithsonian Institution is an independent establishment of the Executive Branch of the government. The United States National Museum is one of eight bureaus of the Smithsonian Institution.

Most of the publications of the Smithsonian Institution are public documents and either are distributed free by the Institution or are sold by the Superintendent of Documents. Exceptions are the *Smithsonian Miscellaneous Collections, Special Publications*, and Vol. 6 of the *Annals of the Astrophysical Observatory of the Smithsonian Institution*, which are available only from the Institution. The series publications of the Institution include the following:

Miscellaneous Collections. These include reports of explorations, summaries of existing knowledge in special fields, lists and synopses of organic and inorganic substances, museum catalogues, and bibliographic aids. They are available only from the Institution. The first one was published in 1862; 111 volumes have appeared to 1950.

Contributions to Knowledge. These are memoirs recording the results of comprehensive original research. They began in 1848 and terminated in 1916 with Vol. 35.

Annual Reports. In addition to administrative information concerning the Institution and its bureaus, each *Annual Report* contains about 30 scientific articles in the Appendix. The prices vary. Reprints of these *Annual Reports* are available from the Institution. The first one was issued for 1847.

Special Publications. These are available only from the Institution; the prices vary.

Explorations and Field Work. These are illustrated accounts of the expeditions sponsored by the Institution. They have been issued annually since 1912.

Quarterly, annual, and occasional classified lists of Smithsonian Institution publications have been issued. *Smithsonian Institution Publication* 478 (1882; also issued as *Miscellaneous Collections*, Vol. 27, Art. 4, and in the *Annual Report* for 1886) is a catalogue of publications from 1846 to 1882. *Smithsonian Institution Publication* 1376 (1903; also issued as *Miscellaneous Collections*, Vol. 44) is a list of publications from 1846 to 1903.

United States National Museum

One of eight bureaus of the Smithsonian Institution, the United States National Museum issues the following series publications:

Bulletins. Many geologic and paleontologic subjects are included in these larger monographic studies. The first was issued in 1875, and a total of 193 was published to 1948.

Proceedings. These are shorter publications of the Museum. They began in 1879, and 3,224 items were published in 98 volumes to 1948. An annual index is given in the annual report of the Museum and is also issued separately.

Reports. Issued annually, these, prior to 1905, contained scientific papers.

Annual and occasional lists of United States National Museum publications have been issued. The annual lists are reprinted from the *Annual*

Reports. *Bulletin* 193 is a comprehensive 306-page list and index of publications from 1875 to 1946; it was issued in 1948 and is sold by the Superintendent of Documents. Earlier lists of publications (with title indexes) were *Bulletin* 51 (1902), covering 1875 to 1900; *Bulletin* 51, Supp. 1 (1906), covering 1901 to 1906; and a separate list (1914) covering 1906 to 1912. An annual index to the *Proceedings* is given in the *Annual Report* of the Museum and is also issued separately.

QUASI-OFFICIAL AGENCIES

Semiofficial institutions, though established by Federal law and partly supported by the government, are maintained largely by private endowments and funds contributed by other organizations. With the present postwar financial support by the United States government of scientific research on a vast scale, the original provisions as to Federal money are becoming of little significance in differentiating between such semiofficial groups and those organizations discussed in the next chapter. The nature of the publications included here does not differ from that of public documents. They are available only from the issuing agency, but so also are some of the publications of regular government agencies such as the Smithsonian Institution.

National Academy of Sciences: National Research Council

At the request of President Wilson during the First World War the National Research Council was organized in 1916 with the cooperation of the National Scientific and Technical Societies of the United States and was established by the National Academy of Sciences under Congressional charter to coordinate the research facilities of the nation for work on military problems involving scientific knowledge. It was reorganized in 1919 as a permanent body by Executive Order 2859 (dated 1918) for the general encouragement of scientific research. It is a cooperative organization of American scientific men, including a representation of men of affairs interested in engineering and industry and in the basic sciences upon which the applications of science depend. Its membership is composed largely of accredited representatives of about 85 national scientific and technical societies. Its essential purpose is the promotion of scientific research and the dissemination and application of scientific knowledge for the benefit of the national strength and well-being.

The following publications are sold by the Publications Office, National Research Council.

Bulletin Series. These are monographs especially prepared by committees of the Council or directories for general use in science compiled by the

Council. At irregular intervals 118 titles had been published to 1949. A discount of 20 per cent from the list price is given to those who subscribe for the series as issued, direct from the Publications Office. Separate numbers are sold at prices based upon the cost of manufacture. The small remaining stock of Nos. 1 to 75 are free upon request.

Reprint and Circular Series. These are papers published or printed by or for the National Research Council. A discount of 20 per cent from the list price is given to subscribers for the series as issued, direct from the Publications Office. A total of 130 titles had been published to 1949; the small remaining stock of Nos. 1 to 100 are free upon request.

Annual Reports. The *Annual Report of the National Research Council* is issued as a part of the *Annual Report of the National Academy of Sciences* and is reprinted for distribution by the National Research Council. No reprints were issued for 1916 or 1917; the following are out of print: 1919, 1921 to 1922, 1924 to 1925, 1925 to 1926, 1927 to 1928, 1928 to 1929, 1936 to 1937.

Committee Reports. These are not available for general distribution.

Miscellaneous Publications. These are publications not issued in series but available from the Publications Office. They include organizational material and lists of members, four periodicals, and reports on various specialized subjects, none in geology.

An indexed and priced "List of Publications" is available upon request; it includes the *Bulletin Series, Reprint and Circular Series, Miscellaneous Publications,* and a "Supplementary List." The latest issue is dated July 1949.

Numerous separate publications have been issued with the sponsorship of the National Research Council or its committees but are published and sold by commercial or other publishers.

American Geophysical Union

The American Geophysical Union cooperates with the Committee on Geophysics of the National Research Council and the American National Committee of the International Union of Geodesy and Geophysics in the publication of studies pertaining to the following sections of the American Geophysical Union: Geodesy, Seismology, Meteorology, Terrestrial magnetism and electricity, Oceanography, Volcanology, Hydrology (since 1931), and Tectonophysics (since 1940).

Transactions have been published since 1921, beginning with Vol. 2. Some years the volumes have been issued as a unit (covering "all sections"), and some years in two, three, or four parts, usually representing various sections but occasionally dealing with special symposiums. Earlier volumes of the *Transactions* (Nos. 2, 4, 6 to 9) were issued as *Bulletins of the National Research Council* (Nos. 17, 41, 53, 56, 61, 68).

Special Publications include *Reprint and Circular Series No.* 11 of the National Research Council and "Bibliography of Hydrology" (1935 to 1940). A price list is issued free.

The figures given for many of these government publications include some not yet released; conversely, a single number may include several parts, each otherwise being an independent publication.

CHAPTER 11

ORGANIZATION BULLETINS

Numerous organizations publish literature of geologic interest besides those which are in some way connected with the United States government. Some are privately endowed research institutions; some are professional societies maintained by their members or federations of such societies; some are academies of science organized along various geographic lines; some are trade associations; some are private business firms; some are colleges and universities; some are museums. Those of the above classes of organization which are statewide in scope, are publicly supported, and have the status of public agencies are discussed in Chap. 12 on State Bulletins, for the same reason that similar groups of national scope were described in Chap. 10 on United States Government Documents. An up-to-date and complete list of such organizations would be difficult to secure; a list of their publications would be much more difficult to compile and would be unnecessary in view of the index guides and bibliographies (Chap. 7) which list them.

Organization bulletins that are entered for United States copyright are listed in Part 1B of *Catalog of Copyright Entries*, now published semiannually by the Library of Congress, Washington, and sold by the Superintendent of Documents.

Important organization bulletins are recorded (usually in smaller type at the bottom of the page) in *Publishers' Weekly*, published by R. R. Bowker Company, New York.

Organization bulletins are included in the *Vertical File Service Catalog*, described on page 180.

GEOLOGIC BULLETINS

The following three directories list organizations that publish geologic literature and indicate to a greater or lesser extent the kinds of publications issued.

"Source Book: A Directory of Public Agencies in the United States Engaged in the Publication of Literature on Mining and Geology" was compiled by Russell C. Fleming and published in 1933 by the American Institute of Mining and Metallurgical Engineers, New York (128 pp.). Ninety-eight agencies are grouped as national societies or bureaus, regional societies or organizations, trade associations, commercial publications, state organizations, universities, etc.

"Directory of Geological Material in North America," by J. V. Howell and A. I. Levorsen, was published in *Bulletin of the American Association of*

Petroleum Geologists, Vol. 30, No. 8, Pt. 2, August 1946, pp. 1321–1432. Publishers are listed by area and then by type of material.

International Geologen- und Mineralogen-Kalender of Deutsche Geologische Gesellschaft was published irregularly by Ferdinand Enke Verlag, Stuttgart. It includes an international directory of geologic organizations and educational institutions, with information as to their publications. The last volume (588 pp.) was issued in 1937.

The following six directories list educational institutions that emphasize, in one manner or another, the geologic sciences. No information is given about their publications. Reference may also be made to the list of educational and research institutions and libraries which are especially important in geographic studies in the United States, given on pages 64 to 65 and 276 to 277 of "Aids to Geographical Research" by John Kirtland Wright and Elizabeth T. Platt, 2d ed., American Geographical Society, New York, 1947.

"Directory of Geology Departments and Departments Including Geology, at Four-Year Colleges and Universities in the United States" was compiled by William F. Read and Delamarcia T. Sandeen and issued by the Association of Geology Teachers, Appleton, Wisconsin (July 1949 ed., 9 pp., processed). It names 243 departments in 241 institutions.

"Directory of Geology Departments of Educational Institutions in the United States and Canada" was compiled by Dorothy Johnson, Shepard W. Lowman, and John T. Rouse and published by the American Association of Petroleum Geologists, Tulsa, 1949 (136 pp.).

"Summer Field Courses in Geology, 1950" was issued as Report 1 by the American Geological Institute, Washington, 1950 (101 pp., processed).

"Directory of Mineral Engineering Schools in the United States and Canada" was published in *Mining Engineering*, Vol. 186, Sec. 2, 1949, pp. 251–252.

"The Domestic Mining Industry of the United States in World War II" by John Davis Morgan, Jr., published in 1949 by the National Security Resources Board, Washington, contains a directory of institutions of higher learning that have regular courses in geology and/or mining engineering, prepared by the American Council on Education. The list is Organization Chart 30, which appears on pages 381 to 405.

Directory of College Geography of the United States was compiled by J. R. Schwendeman and published by the Department of Geography, University of Kentucky, Lexington, Kentucky. The latest issue covers the academic year 1949–1950.

SCIENTIFIC BULLETINS, INCLUDING GEOLOGY

Some of the organizations listed in the following directories publish geologic literature. Other foreign (German, Italian, Polish) and international organizations are enumerated in the directories listed on pages 34 to 37 of "Guide to Reference Books" by Isadore Gilbert Mudge, American Library Association, Chicago (6th ed., 1936). A few other similar directories, especially in the less common languages, are listed on pages 77 to 112 of "Guide to the Cataloguing of the Serial Publications of Societies and Institutions" by Harriet Wheeler Pierson, Library of Congress, Washington (2d ed., 1931, 128 pp.), and on pages 44 to 45 of "Sources of Engineering Information" by Blanche H. Dalton, University of California Press, Berkeley (1948, 109 pp.). To these may be added the "Handbook of the Japanese Societies of Natural Science and Cultural Science," published in 1949 by the Scientific Data Section, Scientific Education Bureau, Ministry of Education, Tokyo (Vol. 1, 45 pp., mimeographed).

Societies and educational institutions

"Handbook of Scientific and Technical Societies and Institutions of the United States and Canada" was compiled by Callie Hull, S. J. Cook, and J. R. Kohr and published as *Bulletin* 115 by the National Research Council, Washington (5th ed., 1948, 371 pp.). Information is given for 1,302 organizations in the United States and 166 in Canada; their serial publications (only) are indicated.

"Industrial Research Laboratories of the United States" was compiled by Callie Hull and published as *Bulletin* 113 by the National Research Council, Washington (8th ed., 1946, 415 pp.). Consulting research laboratories are arranged alphabetically by company name. Universities and colleges offering research services to industry are listed alphabetically by state and institution. The names of periodicals published by these laboratories are given. There is a geographic index, a personnel index, and a subject index; the latter has entries in geophysics, geochemistry, minerals, ores, fuels, metals, and many individual mineral products, especially petroleum and its products.

"A Guide to the Literature of Chemistry," by Crane and Patterson,[1] has in Appendix 5 (pages 273 to 278) a list of scientific and technical organizations, with a list of their serial publications.

"World of Learning 1950," published in London by Europa: George Allen & Unwin, Ltd., is the third edition (875 pp.) of a world-wide guide to universities and colleges, learned societies, scientific institutions, libraries and museums, and art collections.

"Minerva: Jahrbuch der gelehrten Welt" covers research institutions, learned societies, observatories, libraries, archives, museums, universities, and technical high schools (arranged alphabetically by towns), and gives

[1] Crane, E. J., and Austin M. Patterson, "A Guide to the Literature of Chemistry," John Wiley & Sons, Inc., New York, 1927.

information on their publications. The latest edition (thirty-third year-book) was issued in 1938 (Pt. 1, 1,320 pp.; Pt. 2, 1,029 pp.) and published in Berlin and Lepizig by Walter De Gruyter.

Index généralis; annuaire général des universités, grandes écoles, academies, archives, bibliothèques, instituts scientifiques, jardins botaniques et zoologiques, musées, observatoires, sociétés savantes was published in Paris by Gauthier-Villars & Cie, the latest edition (2,830 pp.) being 1939.

Education Directory—Higher Education, 1949–50, Part 3, published by the Office of Education, Federal Security Agency, Washington, is a directory of all institutions of higher education in the United States, Alaska, Canal Zone, Hawaii, and Puerto Rico.

"Europa" contains a directory of scientific organizations in Europe. This is a loose-leaf encyclopedia; Vol. 1 was first issued by Europa Publications, Ltd., London, in 1946.[1]

"Orbis" contains a directory of universities, libraries, museums, and learned societies outside of Europe. Issuance of this loose-leaf encyclopedia by Europa Publications, Ltd., London, began in 1938, and supplementary pages intended for insertion appear at irregular intervals.[2]

"World Universities" is a loose-leaf directory (538 pp.) of universities and colleges throughout the world and is published by British Universities Encyclopaedia, Ltd., London.

"American Universities and Colleges" was edited by A. J. Brumbaugh and published by the American Council on Education, Washington (5th ed., 1948, 1,054 pp.). The institutions are arranged alphabetically, and the classes of publications are given for each.

"Universities of the World outside U.S.A.," edited by Merritt M. Chambers and published in 1950 by the American Council on Education, Washington (924 pp.), is a directory to over 2,000 institutions of higher education outside the United States.

The Official Year-Book of the Scientific and Learned Societies of Great Britain and Ireland was published in 1938 (55th annual issue, 169 pp.) by Charles Griffin & Co., Ltd., London. Section 4 covers Geography, Geology, and Mineralogy. Information is given on publications and their prices.

"Sociedades e Instituciones Cientificas de la América Latina" was published in 1942 by the Pan-American Sanitary Bureau, Washington. The entries are arranged by subject and then by country, and the names of official publications are given when possible.

"Handbook of the Learned and Scientific Societies and Institutions of Latin America," by Henry O. Severance, deals with those organizations

[1] Edwards, Clyde S., Acting Chief, Serials Division, Library of Congress, personal communication, July 18, 1950.
[2] *Idem.*

"which make and have made contributions to knowledge through their publications." It was privately printed (123 pp., processed) in 1940 in Washington. The arrangement is alphabetical by country, town, and organization. For each is given the name, date of founding, and a directory of publications, which are listed to 1940.

"Handbook of Learned Societies and Institutions:.America" was *Publication* 39 of the Carnegie Institution of Washington (1908, 592 pp.). The organizations are arranged alphabetically; a bibliography of the publications of each is included. The index has entries under Geology, Mineralogy, Paleontology, Seismology, Geography, Mining, and Metallurgy.

"Chemical Societies of the Nineteenth Century," by Henry Carrington Bolton, gives the names and serial publications of these organizations. It was published by the Smithsonian Institution, Washington, in 1902 as *Smithsonian Miscellaneous Collections*, Vol. 41, Art. 8 (15 pp.).

"Publications of Societies," edited by R. R. Bowker, is a list of the publications of American scientific, literary, and other societies from their beginning and includes some organizations not represented in other lists. It was issued in 1899 by *Publishers' Weekly*, New York (181 pp.).

"Handbuch der deutschen Wissenschaft" is a two-volume directory of all important universities, schools, institutions, museums, and societies having to do with German science. It also contains a complete list of German scientific periodicals and biographical information about German scientists. It was published in 1950 by F. R. K. Koetschau, Berlin (1,561 pp.).

"Deutsche technisch-wissenschaftliche Forschungstätten," by Karl Boeck, lists and classifies the publications of German scientific societies and research institutes. It was published in two volumes in 1930–1931 by V. D. I. Verlag, Berlin (Vol. 1, 135 pp., Vol. 2, 445 pp.).

"Bibliographie des travaux scientifiques (sciences mathématiques, physiques et naturelles) publiée par les sociétés savantes de la France; dressée sous les auspices du Ministère de l'instruction publique" gives full information about the publications of French scientific societies to 1922. Volume 1 was edited by Joseph Dencker, and Volume 2 by René Descharmes.

"Les resources du travail intellectual en France," by Edme Tassy and Pierre Léris, covers the publications of French professional associations and libraries. It was published in 1921 (711 pp.) by Gauthier-Villars & Cie, Paris, and a supplement (100 pp.) was issued in 1924.

Museums

"The Libraries, Museums and Art Galleries Year Book 1948" was published in 1948 by James Clarke & Co., Ltd., London, and R. R. Bowker

Company, New York (288 pp.). Besides the institutions in Europe, North and South America, Australasia, the Near East, and the Far East, a list of postwar German museums is given.

"Handbook of American Museums" was published in 1932 by the American Association of Museums, Washington; its 779 pages include information on the publications of the museums listed.

"The Museum in America," by Laurence Vail Coleman, was published in 1939 by the American Association of Museums, Washington; Vol. 3 (730 pp.) is a classified directory of museums in the United States.

"Directory of Museums and Art Galleries in Canada" was published in 1932 by The Museums Association, London (92 pp.).

"Directory of Museums in South America," by Laurence Vail Coleman, was published in 1929 by the American Association of Museums, Washington (133 pp.).

"Directory of Museums of the British Isles" was published in 1948 by The Museums Association, London.

"Directory of Museums and Art Galleries in Australia and New Zealand," by S. F. Markham and H. C. Richards, was published in 1934 by The Museums Association, London (115 pp.).

"Directory of Museums and Art Galleries in British Africa, Malta, Cyprus, and Gibraltar" was published in 1933 by The Museums Association, London (61 pp.).

"Museums of India," by S. F. Markham and H. Hargreaves, was published in 1936 by The Museums Association, London (229 pp.).

"Directory of Museums in Ceylon, British Malaya, Hong Kong, Sarawak, British North Borneo, Fiji, West Indies, British Guiana," by S. F. Markham, was published in 1934 by The Museums Association, London (67 pp.).

International organizations

"International Congresses and Conferences, 1840–1937" by Winifred Gregory, published in 1938 by the Bibliographical Society of America (the H. W. Wilson Company, New York), is a union list (229 pp.) of the publications of such organizations.

House organs

An example of a bulletin of geologic interest published at irregular intervals by a commercial firm is *Foote Prints*, issued by Foote Mineral Company, Philadelphia.

Some other house organs of geologic interest published in the United States and Canada are named on pages 1339, 1359, 1369, 1372, 1397, 1412, and 1422 of the "Directory of Geological Material in North America" by

J. V. Howell and A. I. Levorsen, *Bulletin of the American Association of Petroleum Geologists*, Vol. 30, No. 8, Pt. 2, August 1946.

Over 5,100 house organs are listed in "Directory of House Organs," published in 1944 by Printers' Ink Publishing Company, Inc., New York (140 pp.). It has an alphabetical register of titles, alphabetical list of sponsors, geographic list of sponsors (with their addresses) arranged alphabetically by states and towns, and a list of house organs temporarily suspended.

CHAPTER 12

STATE BULLETINS

The states of the United States are significant publishers of geologic bulletins.

Geologic surveys

One of the major sources of geologic literature has long been the state geologic surveys of the United States. The earliest of these, that of Massachusetts, issued its first publication in 1832.

The history of the various state surveys up to 1885 is given and the publications of each to that date are enumerated in "Contributions to a History of American State Geological and Natural History Surveys" by George P. Merrill, *U. S. National Museum Bulletin* 109, 1920.

Another discussion of the publications of the state surveys appeared in *U.S. Geological Survey Bulletin* 465, issued in 1911. Titled "The State Geological Surveys of the United States," it was compiled under the direction of C. W. Hayes and had in the appendix information about a few cooperating state agencies other than geologic surveys.

A later report of similar nature was prepared by means of questionnaires sent out by the Committee on State Geological Surveys of the Division of Geology, and Geography of the National Research Council, under the chairmanship of M. M. Leighton, and published in 1932 as *Bulletin* 88 of the National Research Council. Indicated are the type, scope, and number of publications that have been issued by each state survey.

Somewhat similar information is given about most of the state geologic surveys in Part 5 of "Source Book: A Directory of Public Agencies in the United States Engaged in the Publication of Literature on Mining and Geology," compiled by Russell C. Fleming and published in 1933 by the American Institute of Mining and Metallurgical Engineers, New York.

"State Geological Surveys" by Wilson M. Laird, a chapter in *The American Year Book* for 1949 (published in 1950 by Thomas Nelson & Sons, New York), is a late summary of the scope and activities of the state geologic surveys, covering their organization; their work on basic and economic geology and water resources; their geologic, topographic, and planimetric mapping; their other activities; and their publications. The similar report for 1948 was reprinted in full in *California Journal of Mines and Geology*, Vol. 45, pp. 299–317, 1949.

Tabulated information about the state geologic surveys as of 1948, but without detail regarding their publications, is given in Organization Chart 39 (pages 381 to 405) of "The Domestic Mining Industry of the United States in World War II" by John Davis Morgan, Jr., National Security Resources Board, Washington, 1949.

Most of the state geologic surveys furnish on request price lists of available publications, a few maintain mailing lists for notification about current publications, and some will send catalogues of both available and out-of-print publications. State publications are often distributed free to residents but sold to others.

In communicating with these state geologic surveys, other persons besides the author must surely have been annoyed by the confusion in their names, which appear in numerous forms in different places; some changes in governmental organization occur from time to time, of course, but not so often as the multiplicity of names would indicate. The following directory of state geologic surveys is therefore presented here, using, with permission, information supplied by Edward L. Clark, secretary of the Association of American State Geologists, and obtained also by direct inquiry by the author. Under the name of the state, arranged alphabetically, is given the name of the agency, the name of the broader agency of which it is a part, the title of the officer, and the address. Omissions and inconsistencies prove the need for an even more precise compilation; detailed addresses would be useful for more than mailing purposes. The name of the geologist or other head of the agency is not given because of changes in personnel.

Alabama
    Agency: Geological Survey of Alabama
    Title: State Geologist
    Address: University, Ala.
Arizona
    Agency: Arizona Bureau of Mines
    Within: University of Arizona
    Title: Director
    Address: University of Arizona, Tucson, Ariz.
Arkansas
    Agency: Arkansas Geological Survey
    Within: Resources and Development Commission
    Title: State Geologist
    Address: 446 State Capitol, Little Rock, Ark.
California
    Agency: Division of Mines
    Within: State Department of Natural Resources
    Title: State Mineralogist
    Address: San Francisco 11, Calif.

Colorado
  Agency: Colorado Geological Survey Board
  Title: Secretary
  Address: Colorado School of Mines, Golden, Colo.
Connecticut
  Agency: State Geological and Natural History Survey
  Title: Director
  Address: Trinity College, Hartford 6, Conn.
Florida
  Agency: Florida Geological Survey
  Within: Department of Conservation
  Title: Director
  Address: Tallahassee, Fla.
Georgia
  Agency: Department of Mines, Mining and Geology
  Within: State Division of Conservation
  Title: Director
  Address: 425 State Capitol, Atlanta, Ga.
Hawaii
  Agency: Division of Hydrography
  Within: Department of Public Lands
  Title: Chief Hydrographer
  Address: Honolulu, Hawaii
Idaho
  Agency: Idaho Bureau of Mines and Geology
  Within: University of Idaho
  Title: Director
  Address: University of Idaho, Moscow, Idaho
Illinois
  Agency: State Geological Survey Division
  Within: Department of Registration and Education
  Title: Chief
  Address: Urbana, Ill.
Indiana
  Agency: Division of Geology
  Within: Department of Conservation
  Title: State Geologist
  Address: Bloomington, Ind.
Iowa
  Agency: Iowa Geological Survey Board
  Title: Director and State Geologist
  Address: State University, Iowa City, Iowa
Kansas
  Agency: State Geological Survey of Kansas
  Within: University of Kansas

Title: State Geologist
Address: University of Kansas, Lawrence, Kans.
Kentucky
   Agency: Kentucky Geological Survey
   Within: Geological Department, University of Kentucky
   Title: State Geologist
   Address: University of Kentucky, Lexington, Ky.
Louisiana
   Agency: Louisiana Geological Survey
   Within: Department of Conservation
   Title: State Geologist
   Address: Baton Rouge, La.
Maine
   Agency: Maine Geological Survey
   Within: Maine Development Commission
   Title: State Geologist
   Address: University of Maine, Orono, Maine
Maryland
   Agency: Department of Geology, Mines and Water Resources
   Within: Board of Natural Resources
   Title: Director
   Address: Johns Hopkins University, Baltimore 18, Md.
Michigan
   Agency: Geological Survey Division
   Within: Department of Conservation
   Title: State Geologist
   Address: Lansing, Mich.
Minnesota
   Agency: Minnesota Geological Survey
   Within: University of Minnesota
   Title: Director
   Address: University of Minnesota, Minneapolis 14, Minn.
Mississippi
   Agency: Mississippi State Geological Survey
   Within: State Geological Commission
   Title: State Geologist
   Address: University, Miss.
Missouri
   Agency: Division of Geological Survey and Water Resources
   Within: Bureau of Geology and Mines
   Title: State Geologist
   Address: Rolla, Mo.
Montana
   Agency: Montana Bureau of Mines and Geology
   Within: Montana School of Mines

Title: Director
Address: Montana School of Mines, Butte, Mont.
Nebraska
  Agency: Nebraska Geological Survey
  Within: University of Nebraska
  Title: Director
  Address: University of Nebraska, Lincoln, Neb.
Nevada
  Agency: Nevada State Bureau of Mines
  Within: University of Nevada
  Title: Director
  Address: Mackay School of Mines, Reno, Nev.
New Hampshire
  Agency: Mineral Resources Committee
  Within: New Hampshire State Planning and Development Committee
  Title: Geologist
  Address: Durham, N.H.
New Jersey
  Agency: Division of Geology and Waters
  Within: Department of Conservation and Economic Development
  Title: State Geologist
  Address: Trenton, N.J.
New Mexico
  Agency: New Mexico Bureau of Mines and Mineral Resources
  Within: New Mexico School of Mines
  Title: Director
  Address: New Mexico School of Mines, Socorro, N.M.
New York
  Agency: State Science Service
  Within: State Education Department
  Title: State Geologist
  Address: New York State Museum, Albany, N.Y.
North Carolina
  Agency: Division of Mineral Resources
  Within: Department of Conservation and Development
  Title: State Geologist
  Address: Raleigh, N.C.
North Dakota
  Agency: North Dakota Geological Survey
  Title: State Geologist
  Address: University of North Dakota, Grand Forks, N.D.
Ohio
  Agency: Geological Survey of Ohio
  Within: State Department of Public Works
  Title: State Geologist
  Address: Orton Hall, Ohio State University, Columbus 10, Ohio

Oklahoma
  Agency: Oklahoma Geological Survey
  Within: Oklahoma Planning and Resources Board
  Title: Director
  Address: Norman, Okla.
Oregon
  Agency: State Department of Geology and Mineral Industries
  Title: Director
  Address: 702 Woodlark Building, Portland 5, Ore.
Pennsylvania
  Agency: Topographic and Geologic Survey
  Within: Department of Internal Affairs
  Title: State Geologist
  Address: Harrisburg, Pa.
Rhode Island
  Agency: Mineral Resources Committee
  Within: Industrial Commission
  Title: Chairman
  Address: Providence, R.I.
South Carolina
  Agency: South Carolina Geological Survey
  Title: State Geologist
  Address: University of South Carolina, Columbia 19, S.C.
South Dakota
  Agency: State Geological Survey
  Title: State Geologist
  Address: South Dakota University, Vermillion, S.D.
Tennessee
  Agency: Division of Geology
  Within: Department of Conservation
  Title: State Geologist
  Address: G-5 State Office Building, Nashville 3, Tenn.
Texas
  Agency: Bureau of Economic Geology
  Within: University of Texas
  Title: Director
  Address: University Station, Box B, Austin 12, Tex.
Vermont
  Agency: Vermont Geological Survey
  Within: Vermont Development Commission
  Title: State Geologist
  Address: Burlington, Vt.
Virginia
  Agency: Virginia Geological Survey
  Within: Virginia Conservation Commission
  Title: State Geologist
  Address: Box 1428, University Station, Charlottesville, Va.

Washington
  Agency: Division of Mines and Geology
  Within: Department of Conservation and Development
  Title: Supervisor of Geology
  Address: Olympia, Wash.
West Virginia
  Agency: West Virginia Geological and Economic Survey
  Title: State Geologist
  Address: Morgantown, W.Va.
Wisconsin
  Agency: Wisconsin Geological and Natural History Survey
  Within: University of Wisconsin
  Title: State Geologist
  Address: 115 Science Hall, University of Wisconsin, Madison 6, Wis.
Wyoming
  Agency: Geological Survey of Wyoming
  Title: State Geologist
  Address: University of Wyoming, Laramie, Wyo.

Bureaus of mines

Some of the state bureaus of mines are connected with the state geologic surveys and are included in the preceding list. Others are conducted as entirely separate agencies, sometimes being more active or influential than the corresponding geologic survey and sometimes less. The following directory of state bureaus of mines is compiled mostly from Organization Chart 30, which appears on pages 381 to 405 of "The Domestic Mining Industry of the United States in World War II" by John Davis Morgan, Jr., National Security Resources Board, Washington, 1949. An even worse lack of consistency appears in these names than has already been remarked upon in regard to the state geologic surveys.

State	Name of agency	Title of officer
Alabama	Department of Industrial Relations	Chief, Division of Safety and Inspection
Arizona	Office of State Mine Inspector	State Mine Inspector
Arkansas	Department of Mining	Mine Inspector
California	Department of Natural Resources	State Mineralogist, Division of Mines
Colorado	Bureau of Mines	Commissioner
Connecticut	Connecticut Development Commission	Managing Director
Georgia	Division of Conservation	Director of Mines, Mining, and Geology
Idaho	Bureau of Mines and Geology	Inspector of Mines

State	Name of agency	Title of officer
Illinois	Department of Mines and Minerals	Director
Indiana	Department of Mine Inspection	Director
Iowa	State Mine Inspection Board	Secretary, State Mine Inspectors
Kansas	Labor Department	Chief Mine Inspector
Kentucky	Department of Mines and Minerals	Chief Mine Inspector
Louisiana	Department of Minerals	Commissioner
Maine	Mining Bureau	Secretary
Maryland	Bureau of the Mines	Chief Mine Engineer
Michigan	Conservation Department	State Geologist
Minnesota	Division of Land and Minerals	Director
Mississippi	State Mineral Lease Commission	Secretary
Missouri	Bureau of Mines	Chief Inspector
Montana	Industrial Accident Board	Chairman
Nebraska	Office of State Inspector of Mines	State Inspector of Mines
Nevada	Office of State Mine Inspector	State Mine Inspector
New Jersey	Department of Labor	Chief Mine Inspector
New Mexico	Department of Mine Inspector	State Mine Inspector
New York	Bureau of Mines	Supervising Inspector
North Carolina	Department of Conservation and Development	State Geologist
North Dakota	Office of State Mine Inspector	State Mine Inspector
Ohio	Department of Industrial Relations	Chief, Division of Mines and Mining
Oklahoma	Executive Department	Chief Inspector of Mines
Oregon	Department of Geology and Mineral Industries	Director
Pennsylvania	Department of Mines	Secretary of Mines
South Dakota	Office of Inspector of Mines	Inspector of Mines
Tennessee	Division of Mines	Chief Inspector
Texas	College of Mines and Metallurgy	Inspector of Mines
Utah	Industrial Commission	Commissioner
Vermont	Department of Natural Resources	State Geologist
Virginia	Department of Labor and Industry	Chief Mine Inspector
Washington	Department of Conservation and Development	Superintendent of Mines and Mining
West Virginia	Department of Mines	Chief
Wisconsin	Industrial Commission	Mine Inspector
Wyoming	Land Department	Coal Mine Inspector

Agricultural experiment stations

Two of the most prolific publishers of state documents are the state agricultural experiment stations and the state engineering or mine experiment stations; both of these agencies, which are often located at or associated with state universities, deal with subjects that sometimes are closely related to the field of geology, and so they should be watched for publications of possible geologic interest. Information about them and about their publications can be obtained from the agency concerned.

Publications of geologic interest are often published by the agricultural experiment stations located in each state and territory as listed below.

Alabama	Auburn
Alaska	College
Arizona	Tucson
Arkansas	Fayetteville
California	Berkeley
Colorado	Fort Collins
Connecticut:	
State station	New Haven
Storrs station	Storrs
Delaware	Newark
Florida	Gainesville
Georgia:	
State station	Experiment
Coastal plain station	Tifton
Hawaii	Honolulu
Idaho	Moscow
Illinois	Urbana
Indiana	LaFayette
Iowa	Ames
Kansas	Manhattan
Kentucky	Lexington
Louisiana:	
University station	Baton Rouge
Maine	Orono
Maryland	College Park
Massachusetts	Amherst
Michigan	East Lansing
Minnesota	St. Paul
Mississippi	State College
Missouri:	
College station	Columbia
Fruit station	Mountain Grove
Poultry station	Mountain Grove
Montana	Bozeman

Nebraska... Lincoln
Nevada... Reno
New Hampshire................................... Durham
New Jersey....................................... New Brunswick
New Mexico....................................... State College
New York:
    State station................................ Geneva
    Cornell station.............................. Ithaca
North Carolina:
    State College station........................ Raleigh
North Dakota:
    State College station........................ Fargo
Ohio... Wooster
Oklahoma... Stillwater
Oregon... Corvallis
Pennsylvania..................................... State College
Puerto Rico:
    Federal station.............................. Mayaguez
    College station.............................. Rio Piedras
Rhode Island..................................... Kingston
South Carolina................................... Clemson
South Dakota..................................... Brookings
Tennessee.. Knoxville
Texas.. College Station
Utah... Logan
Vermont.. Burlington
Virginia:
    College station.............................. Blacksburg
    Truck station................................ Norfolk
Washington:
    College station.............................. Pullman
    Western Washington........................... Puyallup
West Virginia.................................... Morgantown
Wisconsin.. Madison
Wyoming.. Laramie

The technical and other publications of these experiment stations are given in the following lists published and distributed free by the Office of Experiment Stations, U.S. Department of Agriculture, Washington.

Bulletin 1199, 1875 to 1920
Bulletin 1199, Supplement 1, 1921 to 1922
Bulletin 1199, Supplement 2, 1923 to 1924
Bulletin 1199, Supplement 3, 1925 to 1926
Miscellaneous Publication 65, 1927 to 1928
Miscellaneous Publication 128, 1929 to 1930

Miscellaneous Publication 181, 1931 to 1932
Miscellaneous Publication 232, 1933 to 1934
Miscellaneous Publication 294, 1935 to 1936
Miscellaneous Publication 362, 1937 to 1938
Miscellaneous Publication 459, 1939 to 1940
Bibliographical Bulletin 4, 1941 to 1942

Universities and colleges

Although they are little different in their activities and publications from the other educational institutions listed in the directories in Chap. 11, state universities and colleges (including mining schools) should be mentioned here. Because of their official nature, their publications are often available free or at low cost. Many of these institutions have associated with them museums and the above-mentioned state geologic surveys, state bureaus of mines, state agricultural experiment stations, and state engineering or mine experiment stations. Their geologic publications take the form of bulletins (usually prepared by one or more members of the faculty), regular books (published by the college or university press, but not necessarily written by a faculty member), and theses and abstracts of theses (discussed in Chap. 17).

A directory of state agencies and officials cooperating with the U.S. Geological Survey in the fields of geology, topography, water resources, and conservation is prepared for free distribution by the Geological Survey. The latest issue (processed, 26 pp.) is dated Jan. 1, 1950. These agencies are the most likely in their respective states to publish geologic literature.

Bibliographies

State publications have been collected and bibliographies and check lists issued by the National Association of State Libraries and by the Committee on Public Documents of the American Library Association. The Committee on Public Administration of the Social Science Research Council launched in 1930 the State Public Document Center Plan to collect, preserve, and organize for efficient research "the public documents and related source material of each state by designating as document centers one or more libraries in each state that seemed particularly qualified to carry on this work and that were willing to assume responsibility for it."[1]

The most complete collection of state documents in America is in the New York Public Library.

There is no single-volume effective check list or bibliography for state

[1] Kuhlman, A. F., The State Document Center Plan, *Public Documents*, p. 69, 1933.

publications since 1900.[1] Since 1910 the Library of Congress has issued its *Monthly Checklist of State Publications* which records in a widely inclusive manner all state geologic and other publications, both printed and processed, that are acquired by the Document Division of the Library of Congress. Indexes are issued annually. From 1910 to 1920 it was called *Monthly List of State Publications*. This publication is sold by the Superintendent of Documents.

Many state publications issued prior to 1900 and the first number of the above publication may be found in "State Publications: A Provisional List of the Official Publications of the Several States of the United States from Their Organization," compiled by Frances B. Hawley and W. N. Seaver under the editorial direction of R. R. Bowker and published by *Publishers' Weekly*, New York. Four parts were issued between 1899 and 1908: Part 1, New England States (1899); Part 2, North Central States (1902); Part 3, Western States and Territories (1905); Part 4, Southern States (1908). This material had appeared earlier as appendixes to the *American Catalog* for 1884 to 1890 and 1890 to 1895.

Lists, catalogues, and directories of the publications of the states and territories are enumerated on pages 17 to 33 of "Government Document Bibliography in the United States and Elsewhere" by James B. Childs (3d ed., 1942), published by the Library of Congress, Washington.

About half of the states have issued, at varying intervals, lists of publications to cover part or all of the period since 1900, but they are not uniform in type or scope.

Check lists of the publications of 10 states have been prepared as masters' theses at the University of Illinois Library School. According to librarian Donna Finger,[2] none of these lists has been published elsewhere. A catalogue of them follows.

"A Bibliographical Study of Arkansas State Publications" by Jim P. Matthews, 1933, 335 pp.

"Official Publications of Florida, 1821–1941" by Dorothy Gwendolyn Lloyd, 1943, 537 pp.

"Indiana State Documents" by Edna Mae Brown, 1930, 87 pp.

"Iowa State Publications" by Helen Stewart, 1937, 360 pp.

"Kansas State Publications since 1898" by Beatrice Howard Holt, 1932, 138 pp.

"Official Publications of the State of Louisiana" by Lucy Brown Foote, 1935, 555 pp.

"Official Publications of the State of Missouri" by Cerilla Elizabeth Saylor, 1941, 375 pp.

"The Official Publications of Nebraska" by Sylvia Carol Gilmore, 1935, 206 pp.

[1] *Ibid.*, p. 19.
[2] Donna Finger, personal communication, June 19, 1947.

"The Official Publications of South Carolina" by Wendell Wayne Smiley, 1939, 78 pp.
"South Dakota State Publications" by Ruth Caroline Krueger, 1936, 180 pp.

Two volumes of a projected State Author Headings Series, planned to cover documents of all the states, have been published by the American Library Association, Chicago. These are

"Author Headings for the Official Publications of the State of Alabama" by Anne Ethelyn Markley, 1948, 141 pp.
"Author Headings for the Official Publications of the State of Louisiana" by Lucy B. Foote, 1949, 125 pp.

A few similar lists prepared elsewhere for other states are recorded in "Library Literature" and its predecessors (see page 22).

Information on many aspects of state documents, including bibliographic aids, is given in "Manual on the Use of State Publications," edited by James K. Wilcox and published in 1940 by the American Library Association, Chicago.

CHAPTER 13

COUNTY AND CITY BULLETINS

The 3,069 counties of the United States (including parishes in Louisiana) are insignificant publishers of material of geologic interest. Besides numerous maps, however, which are discussed separately in Chap. 19, an occasional bulletin on mines or mining is issued by a county. Other geologic publications are produced mostly by organizations or institutions, such as museums, whose functions are only incidentally related to ordinary county activities.

The only comprehensive list of county publications is "The Official Publications of American Counties: A Union List. With an Introduction on the Collecting of County Publications" by James Goodwin Hodgson, Fort Collins, Colorado, 1937 (processed). It lists over 5,000 county publications in all states and indicates by code at which of 184 libraries they may be consulted. In the index appear 11 items under Mining (which includes one California publication on gems and commercial minerals) and under Inspector of mines in Yavapai County, Arizona; San Diego County, California; Dickinson, Gogebic, Houghton, Iron, and Marquette counties, Michigan; and Crow Wing, Itasca, and St. Louis counties, Minnesota. Among the publications issued by Los Angeles County, California, are those of the Los Angeles County Museum of History, Science and Art, which include *Science Series* No. 692 and *Miscellaneous Publication* No. 734, both on paleontology.

Publications of cities, towns, and other local governments are in general even less likely than county publications to be of geologic interest. In some cities, however, museums under municipal jurisdiction issue publications on geology that may properly be considered among city documents. Most such publications are included in the regular index guides and bibliographies (Chap. 7) and abstract journals (Chap. 8), but some are overlooked in these places, being referred to only among lists of exclusively municipal documents.

Regarded as being issued by semiofficial agencies of the city, scientific and other publications of the museums of New York City are listed in *Municipal Reference Library Notes*, which has been issued monthly (except July and August) since 1914 by the New York Public Library. This bulletin is prepared by the Municipal Reference Library, New York, for circulation among officials and employees of the city of New York and may be purchased by others. Institutions included are the American Museum of Natural History (a leading institution for geologic education), the Brooklyn Institute of Arts and Sciences, and the Staten Island Institute of Arts and Sciences.

Other cities in the United States, including Chicago and Boston, issue, in various forms, periodic check lists of municipal publications but not on a scale, as described above, that will permit their serving as guides to city bulletins of a geologic nature.

A directory of county and city agencies and officials cooperating with the U. S. Geological Survey in the fields of geology, topography, water resources, and conservation is prepared for free distribution by the Geological Survey, Washington. The latest issue (processed, 26 pp.) is dated Jan. 1, 1950. As evidenced by their collaboration with the Federal survey, these agencies are the most likely in their respective counties and cities to publish geologic literature. Inquiries regarding the geology of these areas could profitably be addressed to the officials listed in this directory.

CHAPTER 14

BULLETINS OF OTHER COUNTRIES

A greater tendency exists in English-speaking countries than in others to publish research in the form of independent bulletins rather than in periodicals.[1] This tendency is partly exaggerated by the fact that English-language bulletins are more abundantly distributed in the United States because they are more widely read. On the other hand, certain foreign bulletins are likely to be published in English or reprinted into English and so come to our attention, whereas the reverse situation is almost entirely unknown. In their statistical evaluation of the periodical literature, P. K. L. Gross and A. O. Woodward[2] recorded the fact that foreign-government publications are rarely used by American geologists.

The deplorable condition of foreign-government publications before the First World War (except in Great Britain and the British possessions), the lack of centralization, and the frequent exclusion of important publications from the otherwise inclusive and well-organized national bibliographies have been referred to by James B. Childs.[3]

It is essential to mention here that the official as well as nonofficial geologic literature of these countries is included in *Bibliography of North American Geology*, published by the U.S. Geological Survey (see page 57) and *Bibliography and Index of Geology Exclusive of North America*, published by the Geological Society of America (see page 57).

The bulletins of Canada are discussed here first, followed by those of Great Britain and the British Empire. The Latin-American countries are covered next, beginning with Mexico, the most northerly of them. The nations of continental Europe and those of Asia are discussed last. This chapter concludes with a comprehensive directory of the geologic surveys of all the nations of the world.

Canada

The King's Printer, Department of Public Printing and Stationery, Ottawa, publishes free an *Annual Catalogue* and quarterly supplements listing all printed government publications sold by that office. Most of

[1] Crane, E. J., and Austin M. Patterson, "A Guide to the Literature of Chemistry," p. 132, John Wiley & Sons, Inc., New York, 1927.

[2] Gross, P. K. L., and A. O. Woodward, Serial Literature Used by American Geologists, *Science*, Vol. 73, pp. 660–664, 1931.

[3] Childs, James B., Some Unsolved Bibliographical Problems, *Public Documents*, p. 194, 1933.

the government departments also issue lists of their processed publications, often including the printed ones as well.

A fairly full list of Dominion documents, classified by departments, and a partial list of provincial documents, classified by agency, have been published quarterly since November 1933 as "Recent Government Publications" in the *Ontario Library Review*, issued in Toronto by the Public Libraries Branch of the Ontario Department of Education. The February numbers list the regular weekly and monthly documents.

Other lists and catalogues of Canadian documents are given in "Canadian Government Publications: A Manual for Librarians" by Marion Villiers Higgins, American Library Association, Chicago (1935, 582 pp.), and on pages 42 to 43 of "Government Document Bibliography in the United States and Elsewhere" by James B. Childs, Library of Congress, Washington (3d ed., 1942).

Information on Canadian geology may be secured from the Mines, Forests and Scientific Services, Department of Mines and Resources, Ottawa. This office also provides both printed and processed publications lists. Information on mining and minerals may be secured direct from the Department of Mines and Resources, Ottawa, which also issues the same types of lists of publications. Mineral production data and lists of publications may be secured from the Dominion Bureau of Statistics, Ottawa, which likewise issues summaries of such data for the provinces.

The Geological Survey of Canada is the oldest official scientific organization in the country, having been founded in 1842. Besides its geologic mapping and investigations, it also supervised the geologic aspects of the mining industry and collected and exhibited geologic material. The latter duty—which by Act of Parliament in 1890 was expanded to include material pertaining to paleontology, anthropology, and archaeology—was centralized in 1922 and designated in 1927 as the National Museum of Canada, now part of the Department of Mines and Resources, of which the Geological Survey is also an agency. The Geological Survey continued as a more or less independent agency from 1842 to 1907, when it was incorporated into the Department of Mines, although it reported to the Secretary of State from 1869 to 1873 and to the Minister of the Interior from 1873 to 1890. In 1880 the headquarters were transferred from Montreal to Ottawa. The Division of Geology, Division of Mineralogy, and Division of Palaeontology of the National Museum of Canada are maintained in conjunction with the Geological Survey.

The following classes of publications have been issued by the Geological Survey of Canada.

Memoirs. These deal with regional geology and reconnaissance and special mineral products.

Economic Geology Series. These deal with Canadian metallic and non-metallic mineral deposits; 15 have been published to 1951.

Geological Survey Papers. These are largely preliminary reports and preliminary geologic maps. Most of those out of print have been or are being superseded by more recent publications.

Geological Survey Bulletins. This new series contains reports that do not fall readily into the other classes of publications and particularly those dealing with "problems or events of interest such as are encountered so frequently by the geologist in the course of his field work"; 15 have been published to 1951.

Guide Books. These were prepared in connection with the twelfth session of the International Geological Congress held in Canada in 1913. Each of the eight describes the physiography, geology, and mineral deposits of a different part of Canada. (*Guide Books* Nos. 6 and 7 were issued by the Ontario Bureau of Mines, Toronto, Ontario.)

Summary Reports. These were issued annually from 1916 to 1933. All except 1916 are divided into several parts.

Reports of Progress. These were issued only from 1842 to 1885.

Annual Reports. These were issued only from 1885 to 1904. Administrative statements of the Geological Survey, the Department of Mines, and the National Museum of Canada from 1921 to 1936 are found in the *Annual Reports* of the Department of Mines. Those for the Mines and Geology Branch since 1937 are found in the *Annual Report* of the Department of Mines and Resources and have been reprinted separately.

Application for publications should be addressed to Bureau of Geology and Topography, Mines and Geology Branch, Department of Mines and Resources, Ottawa. If a number of publications are requested, a charge is normally made for each. Remittance should be made by postal note or money order in Canada or postal money order in the United States, made payable to the Receiver General of Canada.

The authoritative directory of Geological Survey publications to 1917 is "Annotated Catalogue of and Guide to the Publications of the Geological Survey, Canada, 1845–1917" by W. F. Ferrier and Dorothy J. Ferrier, issued in 1920 as *Publication* No. 1723 of the Bureau of Geology and Topography. It has been supplemented by the current list "Publications (1909 to 1947 inclusive) of the Geological Survey and National Museum," which may be obtained free upon request from the Bureau of Geology and Topography.

The Bureau of Mines is part of the Mines, Forests and Scientific Services Branch of the Department of Mines and Resources, which was constituted in 1936 and reorganized in 1947. It succeeded the Department of Mines, which was established in 1907 to replace the office of Superintendent of Mines, created in the Department of the Interior in 1884 to supervise the inspection and leasing of mining lands and to establish assay offices where needed. Mineral lands in the Northwest Territories, the Yukon, and the national parks are administered by the Lands and Development Services Branch of the Department of Mines and Resources, and the sale and leasing of lands in the Indian reservations are handled by the Indian Affairs Services Branch.

The Mines and Geology Branch, Bureau of Mines, publishes a "Catalogue and Index of Bureau of Mines Reports," the seventeenth edition of which was issued in 1946 as *Report* 818 and which includes a list of mimeographed "Memorandum Series" and an outline of lists of mines and metallurgical plants. A supplement was issued in October 1949.

The Department of Mines and Resources issues free current price lists for its various agencies, including the Geological Survey and the Bureau of Mines. The illustrations and maps in the publications of the Geological Survey and the Bureau of Mines are elaborately indexed in "Cross-Index to the Maps and Illustrations of the Geological Survey and the Mines Branch (Bureau of Mines) of Canada, 1843–1946 (incl.)," by Carl Faessler, published in 1947 as *Géologie et minéralogie contribution* 75 by Université Laval, Quebec.

Other agencies of the Canadian government that publish literature of especial interest to geologists include the following:

Department of Mines and Resources
  National Parks Branch. Includes the former Dominion Parks Branch, Canadian National Parks Branch, and Rocky Mountain National Parks Branch.
  Surveys and Mapping Bureau. Includes the former Dominion Lands Survey, Surveys Branch, Topographical Survey, Topographical Surveys Branch, and Topographical and Air Survey.
  Geodetic Survey and International Boundary Commission. Includes the former Surveys Branch, Geodetic Survey, and International Boundary Commission.
National Research Council of Canada
Geographic Board of Canada
Special International Niagara Board

The earlier organizational history of these agencies, as well as others now defunct, is given in "Canadian Government Publications" by Marion Villiers Higgins, American Library Association, Chicago, 1935, 588 pp.

Each of the nine provinces of Canada and Yukon Territory issues publications of geologic interest. Lists of current or past publications are issued at intervals by the King's Printer in some of the provinces, but they are not uniform in scope and arrangement. Most of the provincial departments issue lists of their processed publications, often including the printed ones as well. Information on sources of provincial documents is included in the annual volumes of *The Canada Year Book*, published by the Dominion Bureau of Statistics, Ottawa.

Information on the geology of the several provinces may be secured from the following offices:[1]

Alberta.....................	Department of Mines and Minerals, Edmonton
British Columbia..........	Department of Mines, Victoria
Manitoba.................	Department of Mines and Natural Resources, Winnipeg
New Brunswick...........	Department of Lands and Mines, Fredericton
Newfoundland (including Labrador)...............	Department of Natural Resources, St. John's
Nova Scotia..............	Department of Mines, Parliament Buildings, Halifax
Ontario...................	Geological Branch, Department of Mines, Parliament Buildings, Toronto
Prince Edward Island......	Provincial Government Offices, Charlottetown
Quebec...................	Geological Surveys Branch, Department of Mines, Quebec
Saskatchewan.............	Department of Natural Resources and Industrial Development, Regina
Yukon and Northwest Territories..................	Department of Resources and Development, Ottawa

Information on mining and minerals of the provinces may be secured from the following offices.

Alberta....................	Same as above
British Columbia..........	Same as above
New Brunswick...........	Same as above
Nova Scotia..............	Same as above
Saskatchewan.............	Same as above
Manitoba.................	Mines Branch, Department of Mines and Natural Resources, Winnipeg
Ontario...................	Department of Mines, Parliament Buildings, Toronto
Quebec...................	Department of Mines, Quebec

Information on the petroleum resources of the provinces may be secured from the offices listed under mining and minerals, except

British Columbia..........	Department of Lands and Forests, Victoria

Summaries of mineral and petroleum production data, both national and provincial, may be secured from the Dominion Bureau of Statistics, Ottawa.

[1] *The Canada Year Book 1948-49*, Dominion Bureau of Statistics, Ottawa, 1949.

Great Britain

The printing and distribution of British publications are centralized in His Majesty's Stationery Office, London. British government publications can be purchased in the United States (and its possessions and territories) from British Information Services, New York. This agency will prepare special bibliographies upon request and has issued some bibliographies for general distribution. Upon application, one may be placed on its mailing list to receive free publications.

An extensive list of British government agencies and their subdivisions which have issued publications is given in Vol. 58 of "A Catalog of Books Represented by Library of Congress Printed Cards," published in 1944 by Edwards Bros., Inc., Ann Arbor, Michigan.

An annual list of British documents that are sold by the Stationery Office is the *Consolidated List of Government Publications*, which began in 1922 as a consolidation of separate quarterly lists for parliamentary papers and Stationery Office publications. (The 1922 title was *Consolidated List of Parliamentary and Stationery Office Publications*.) It was issued from 1922 to 1935 as the annual cumulative number (No. 12) of the *Monthly List of Government Publications*.

A monthly list of British documents that are sold by the Stationery Office is *Government Publications Issued during the Month*, which began in January 1936 as a consolidation of *Monthly List of Government Publications* and *Monthly Circular of Recent Selected Publications*. The first part of the booklet contains descriptive notes on the chief publications of the month. The catalogue is divided into Parliamentary and non-Parliamentary publications, the latter being listed according to department. Periodicals which appear regularly once a month or oftener are now listed in a separate section of the catalogue, as are reissues. An annual cumulation is issued as *Government Publications: Consolidated List*, which is issued free to regular purchasers of government publications at the end of each year.

A mimeographed *Daily List of Government Publications* is distributed by the Stationery Office.

Separate price lists arranged by departments and subjects (including Geological Survey and Museum, Mines, and Scientific and industrial research) are issued from time to time. The last cumulative consolidated sales catalogue of non-Parliamentary publications was the 352-page "Catalogue of Works . . ." revised to Dec. 31, 1920, and published in 1921.

A 125-page "List of Memoirs, Maps, Sections etc., published by the Geological Survey of Great Britain and the Museum of Practical Geology to 31st December, 1936" was issued in 1937 by the Stationery Office. It has been superseded by Sectional List 45, "Geological Survey and Museum." Publications issued before 1945 are sold only by His Majesty's Stationery Office; those issued since 1945 can also be purchased from the Geological Museum, South Kensington.

Other lists of British documents, covering earlier years and other types of publications, are given on pages 51 to 56 of "Government Document Bibliography in the United States and Elsewhere" by James B. Childs, Library of Congress (3d ed., 1942).

British government publications are included each week in *The British National Bibliography*, begun in January 1950 and described on page 180. The most important British government publications are listed weekly in *The Bookseller*, monthly in *Current Literature*, and quarterly in *Whitaker's Cumulative Book List* (with a separate section on government publications), which are published by J. Whitaker and Sons, Ltd., London (see page 180). Government publications are also listed weekly in *Publishers' Circular and Booksellers' Record* and annually in *The English Catalogue of Books*, both published by The Publishers' Circular, Ltd., Beckenham, Kent (see page 180).

Republic of Ireland

Publication and distribution of the documents of the Republic of Ireland are centralized in the Stationery Office at Dublin.

Weekly lists are printed in *Iris Oifigiüil*, the official gazette. Monthly lists are issued separately by the Stationery Office. Annual lists have been issued beginning with 1924 (1925). Consolidated lists have been issued each 3 years since 1922 to 1925 (1927). Lists were also published covering publications prior to Sept. 1, 1923.[1] The National Library of Ireland has issued since 1927 to 1929 (1930) a "List of Publications Deposited under the Terms of the Industrial and Commercial Property Act," a list of copyrighted publications which includes a section of "Official Publications Issued by the Stationery Office."

Union of South Africa

All official South African publications are included in the monthly accessions list called *Publications Acquired in Terms of Act No. 9 of 1916 (Copyright Act)*, issued in Pretoria by the State Library. Current price lists of sales publications are issued by the Printing and Stationery Department, Pretoria.

Australia

The Commonwealth National Library, Canberra, has issued since 1937 an *Annual Catalogue of Australian Publications*, a complete record of

[1] Childs, James B., "Government Document Bibliography in the United States and Elsewhere," 3d ed., Library of Congress, Washington, 1942.

commonwealth, state, and territorial publications; the first issue (1936), under the same title, was limited to national publications only.

New Zealand

A selected list of official New Zealand publications has been included since 1933–1934 in the annual lists of copyright publications issued in Wellington by the General Assembly Library. The Government Stationery Office at Wellington issues current price lists of sales publications. Earlier documents are listed in other publications enumerated on pages 66 to 67 of "Government Document Bibliography in the United States and Elsewhere" by James B. Childs, Library of Congress, Washington (3d ed., 1942).

British Colonies

A complete list of publications of British Colonies is issued monthly in London by the Colonial Office under the title *Crown Agents for the Colonies: Lists of Publications: Additions during. . . .*

Colonial Reports: Annual is a less complete list, including important publications, both official and unofficial, relating to each colony. It is published annually for each colony by the Colonial Office.

The "Subject Catalogue of the Library of the Royal Empire Society," by Evans Lewin, is a detailed bibliography of British Empire publications since 1910, with a selection of earlier ones. Four of the five volumes have been published (1930 to 1937) as follows.

Volume 1. British Empire, Africa.
Volume 2. Australia, New Zealand, South Pacific, Voyages and travels, Arctic, Antarctic.
Volume 3. Canada, Newfoundland, West Indies, Colonial America.
Volume 4. Mediterranean colonies, Middle East, Indian Empire, Burma, Ceylon, British Malaya, East Indian islands, Far East.

An unpublished list of Colonial publications is the "Catalogue of the Library of the Colonial Office."

From April 1927 to January 1932 the Royal Empire Society issued *Overseas Official Publications*, a quarterly bulletin of official publications received by the Society and issued in the overseas British Empire or relating to it.

Current issues of the *Blue Book* list government publications of the following colonies: Bahamas, Barbados, Bermuda, British Guiana, British Honduras, British Solomon Islands, Ceylon, Cyprus, Fiji, Gambia, Gibraltar, Gold Coast, Kenya, Leeward Islands, Malta, Nigeria, Palestine, St. Vincent, Seychelles, Sierra Leone, Straits Settlements, Tanganyika, Uganda, and Zanzibar.

Mexico

"Mexican Government Publications: A Guide to the More Important Publications of the National Government of Mexico, 1821–1936," by Annita Melville Ker, was published in 1940 by the Library of Congress, Washington. Publications on natural resources (*riquezas naturales*) are classified under executive activities (*poder ejecutivo*).

Central and South America

Important information on the publications of the other Latin-American countries is given in the separate volumes of *A Guide to the Official Publications of the Other American Republics*, which have been issued as parts of the Latin-American Series of the Library of Congress. These guides were begun in 1941 under the sponsorship of the Interdepartmental Commission on Scientific and Cultural Cooperation of the Department of State. They are lists of official publications, including monographs, series, and serials, from the time of independence to 1946, as recorded in the catalogues of the Library of Congress.

The arrangement of the guides is based on the structure of the governments themselves, and the publications are listed according to the agencies and offices of each of the three branches of government—executive, legislative, and judicial. Under each agency are given (1) *Memorias* or *Informes*, (2) serials, and (3) monographs, listed first by agency and second by individual author. Any publication not easily classified under one of the administrative agencies is placed in the appendix, with the issuing bureaus or subordinate agencies arranged in alphabetical order.

The guides themselves are numbered alphabetically by the name of the country, but the numbers of the Latin-American Series correspond to the order in which they were actually issued. An outline is found on page 158.

Some publications that are not included in the above guides because they were not in the holdings of the Library of Congress are noted in "Bibliography of Official Publications and the Administrative Systems in Latin American Countries" by James Bennett Childs, Library of Congress, Washington (1938).[1]

For information on publications after 1946, *Handbook of Latin American Studies* should be consulted. This has been issued since 1936 by the Harvard University Press, Cambridge, Massachusetts, and records annually a selected list of publications (including official ones) according to subject.

The latest information on Latin-American publications may be found

[1] Francisco Aguilera, Acting Director, The Hispanic Foundation, Reference Department, Library of Congress, personal communication, Dec. 18, 1947.

by consulting the Government Publications Recording Room of the Library of Congress, Washington.

Some of the chief publications of the Latin-American countries are listed and sometimes described in *Bulletin of the Pan-American Union*, which is published monthly by the Pan-American Union, Washington.

A much more comprehensive listing, often with annotations, of Latin-American publications formerly appeared in *Ibero-Amerikanisches Archiv*, a quarterly publication of the Ibero-Amerikanisches Institut, Berlin.

Latin-American Series No.	Guide No.	Country	Compiler	Year	Pages
9	1	Argentina	James B. Childs	1945	124
10	2	Bolivia	James B. Childs	1945	66
35	3	Brazil	John De Noia	1949	223
17	4	Chile	Otto Neuburger	1947	94
33	5	Colombia	James B. Childs	1948	89
24	6	Costa Rica	Henry V. Besso	1947	92
11	7	Cuba	James B. Childs	1945	40
25	8	Dominican Republic	John De Noia	1947	40
31	9	Ecuador	John De Noia	1947	56
19	10	El Salvador	John De Noia	1947	64
30	11	Guatemala	Henry V. Besso	1947	86
23	12	Haiti	Otto Neuburger	1947	25
29	13	Honduras	Otto Neuburger	1947	29
27	14	Nicaragua	John De Noia	1947	33
22	15	Panama	John De Noia	1947	34
15	16	Paraguay	James B. Childs	1947	61
36	17	Peru	John De Noia	1949	90
37	18	Uruguay	John De Noia and Glenda Crevenna	1949	91
34	19	Venezuela	Otto Neuburger	1949	59

France

French government publications are marked with an asterisk in Part I of *Bibliographie de la France*, issued weekly by Cercle de la librairie, Paris.

French Colonies

Public Documents of the French Colonies, by José Meyer (*Public Documents*, pp. 97–128, 1938), should be referred to for a guide to the complicated maze of publications of a bureau-ridden administrative setup. Three groups—mandates, protectorates, and colonies proper—are discussed. The publications may also be grouped under the ministries responsible for their administration. The French themselves prefer natural geographic groups.

Germany

Published by the Deutsche Bückerei at Leipzig, the *Monatliches Verzeichnis der reichsdeutschen amtlichen Druckschriften* began in January 1928. It was a monthly list of German official and semiofficial publications, national, state, and municipal, arranged according to the government department. Monthly and annual indexes were issued, until this catalogue expired in 1945.

From 1928 to 1930 the Prussian State Library (Staatsbibliothek) at Berlin issued a semiannual accessions list of German official publications, covering 1927 and the first half of 1929 and including the same political units as the above publication. The material was arranged differently, however, and geologic publications appeared under Geologische landesämter.[1]

Other lists and catalogues of German documents are given on pages 49 to 51 of "Government Document Bibliography in the United States and Elsewhere" by James B. Childs, Library of Congress, Washington (3d ed., 1942).

Sweden

Beginning with a volume covering 1931 to 1933 a catalogue of Swedish official publications, listed alphabetically by agency, with an author and subject index, has been issued annually since 1934 by the Parliamentary Library under the title *Arsbibliografi över sveriges offentiliga publikationer*. Other lists of publications are given on pages 73 to 74 of "Government Document Bibliography in the United States and Elsewhere" by James B. Childs, Library of Congress, Washington (3d ed., 1942).

Netherlands

An annual list of official Netherlands publications, listed alphabetically by agency, with author and subject indexes, is *Nederlandsche Overheidsuitgaven*, issued by the Royal Library (Koninklijke Bibliotheek) in 's-Gravenhage, beginning in 1929. Publications include those of the provinces and Dutch colonies, as well as those of the Royal Academy of Science, the state universities, and the technical colleges. A 234-page indexed sales catalogue of all available publications was issued in 1939.

Italy

Printing and distribution of Italian documents have been centralized since 1923 in the office of the State Purveyor General (Provveditorato Generale dello Stato) in the Ministry of Finance. Current publica-

---

[1] Childs, James B., A Foundation For Foreign Government Document Bibliography, *Public Documents*, p. 196, 1933.

tions are listed with the monthly indexes to the *Gazetta ufficiale del regno d'Italia.*

A list of government publications covering 1861 to 1923 is "Pubblicazioni edite dallo stato o col suo concorso (1861–1923)," issued in 1924. The list was arranged by subject groups corresponding to the ministries existing in 1924. Supplements have been issued to cover 1924 to 1930 and 1931 to 1935.

A newer subject catalogue is "Catalogo delle pubblicazioni legislativo," issued in 1949 but confined almost entirely to prewar documents.[1]

Other lists and catalogues of Italian documents are given on pages 61 to 62 of "Government Document Bibliography in the United States and Elsewhere" by James B. Childs, Library of Congress, Washington (3d ed., 1942).

Switzerland

Documents published by the national government, the cantons, and the communes are arranged alphabetically by agency in *Bibliographie der schweizerischen Amtsdruckschriften (Bibliographie des publications officielles suisses).* It is issued annually, with an author and subject index, by Schweizerische Landesbibliothek, Berne.

India and Pakistan

Memoir 77 (129 pp.) of the Geological Survey of India is "Catalogue of Publications of the Geological Survey of India and Index of Geological Maps," issued in Calcutta in 1948.

In view of their complexity, Indian documents are remarkably well recorded. Since 1927 the Government of India Central Publication Branch, Civil Lines, has issued at Delhi an annual *List of Nonconfidential Publications Not Included in the General Catalogue of Government of India Publications*, continuing previous separate lists for the various departments and provinces, guides to which are enumerated under the name of the geographic entity in Part 4, pages 34 to 76, of "Government Document Bibliography in the United States and Elsewhere" by James B. Childs, Library of Congress, Washington (3d ed., 1942). The same publishing office also issues a general catalogue of current sales publications. The Office of the High Commissioner for India issues in London a mimeographed monthly *List of Publications Received in the Publications Branch during. . . .* "A Short Catalogue" of 535 pages was issued in 1933. Other lists and catalogues of Indian documents and lists of earlier documents

[1] Worley, Parker, Current National Bibliographies II, *Library of Cong. Quart. Jour. of Current Acquisitions,* Vol. 7, No. 1, p. 20, 1949.

are given on pages 57 to 60 of "Government Document Bibliography in the United States and Elsewhere," by James B. Childs, Library of Congress, Washington (3d ed., 1942).

No list of publications has yet (1950) been issued by the new nation of India.[1] A brief list of official documents of Pakistan is *Catalogue of Government of Pakistan Publications* issued irregularly at Karachi.[2]

Indo-China

A catalogue of the geologic publications of Indo-China was issued in Hanoi in 1931 by the Service géologique de l'Indochine.

Japan

In 1927 the Imperial Cabinet Printing Office of Japan began to publish a quarterly catalogue of official publications, *Kancho kankô tosho mokuroku*, changed in 1937 to *K. k. t. geppô*. It was arranged first by departments and then by subject groups. It included publications of Chosen, Hokkaido, the prefectures, and of the imperial universities and schools. Some publications listed were printed in English and other European languages, but most are in Japanese.

The documents of other nations are catalogued or described in publications that are listed in Section 4, pages 34 to 76, of "Government Document Bibliography in the United States and Elsewhere" by James B. Childs, Library of Congress, Washington (3d ed., 1942), and in "Official Publications of European Governments" by José Meyer, published by the American Library in Paris (1926; partly revised, Part 1, 1929). A comprehensive directory of current documents issued by practically every nation is included in the quarterly issues of "Current National Bibliographies" by Parker Worley, published by the Library of Congress, Washington, and described on page 182.

By far the most extensive catalogue of foreign bulletins is the "List of the Serial Publications of Foreign Governments," edited by Winifred Gregory and published in 1932 by the H. W. Wilson Company, New York. Its 720 pages contain the "serial publications of national governments and of such of their states as are to some extent self-governing; namely, the states of Germany, of Austria, of some of the South American Republics, and those of the cantons of Switzerland." The arrangement is alphabetical by country, under each of which are the dependent subdivisions; dominions, colonies, and protectorates are entered under their

[1] Hobbs, Cecil, Reference Librarian for Southeast Asia, Library of Congress, personal correspondence, Feb. 10, 1950.

[2] *Ibid.*

own names. Official gazettes are listed first, followed by the entries for agencies in alphabetical order. The Russian section, compiled by the Division of Documents of the Library of Congress, is especially important because of its completeness (to 1932) and its annotations. The holdings of 85 libraries in the United States and Canada are indicated.

Directory of geologic surveys

The following directory of the geologic surveys of every nation in the world outside the United States has been furnished by Julian D. Sears, Acting Director of the U.S. Geological Survey. All these surveys are publishing material of some consequence, but no postwar information is available about Rumania and Yugoslavia.

Algeria
   Service de la carte géologique
   Boulevard Baudin 14
   Algiers
Anglo-Egyptian Sudan
   Geological Survey
   P.O. Box 410
   Khartoum
Argentina
   Direccion General de Minas, Geologia e Hidrologia
   Peru 562
   Buenos Aires
Australia
   Mineral Resources Survey
   Melbourne Building
   Canberra, A.C.I.

   New South Wales
      New South Wales Geological Survey
      P. O. Box 48
      Sydney
   Queensland
      Geological Survey of Queensland
      Old Railway Offices
      George Street
      Brisbane B4
   South Australia
      Geological Survey of South Australia
      Flinders Street
      Adelaide
   Tasmania
      Tasmania Department of Mines

Darey Street
Hobart
Victoria
Victoria Department of Mines
Melbourne
Western Australia
Geological Survey of Western Australia
Beaufort Street
Perth
Austria
Geologische Bundesanstalt
Rasumofskygasse 23
Wien III/40
Belgian Congo
Service géologique régional de Leopoldville
B.P. 241, Leopoldville
Belgium
Service géologique de la Belgique
13, rue Jenner (Parc Léopold)
Brussels
Brazil
Departamento Nacional da Produção Mineral
Avenida Pasteur 404
Rio de Janeiro
British Guiana
Geological Survey Department
251 Thomas and Murray Streets
Georgetown 4
Canada
Geological Survey of Canada
Department of Mines and Resources
Ottawa, Ontario
China
National Geological Survey of China
942 Chukiang Road
Nanking, Kiangsu
Colombia
Servicio geologico nacional
Apartado Nacional Num. 2504
Bogota
Cuba
Director de montes, minas y aquas
Ministerio de Agricultura
Habana
Czechoslovakia
Statni Geologicky Ustav

Hladkov 6
Praha XVIII
Denmark
Danmarks Geologiske Undersogelse
Charlottenlund
Egypt
Geological Survey of Egypt
Dawawin Post Office
Cairo
Finland
Geologinen Tutkimuslaitos
Kirjasto
Bulevardi 29
Helsinki K
France
Service de la carte géologique de la France
62, Boulevard Saint Michel
Paris (VI)
French Africa
Service des mines
Gouvernement général de l'Afrique Equatorial
Brazzaville
Afrique Equatorial Française

Direction des mines
Boite postale No. 355
Dakar, Senegal
French West Africa
Germany (Surveys in operation in Western Zone)
Badische Geologische Landesanstalt
Elasässertrasse 2
17b Freiburg i.B.

Bayerische Geologische Landesamt
Prinzregentstrasse 26
Munich 22

Württemberg Statistisches Landesamts
Geologische Abteilung
Buchsenstrasses 54
Stuttgart

Hessisches Landesamt für Bodenforschung
Parkstrasse 28
Wiesbaden

Gold Coast
  Gold Coast Geological Survey
  P. O. Box 98
  Saltpond
Great Britain
  Geological Survey and Museum
  Department of Scientific and Industrial Research
  Exhibition Road
  South Kensington
  London, S.W. 7, England

  (Scottish Branch—under Assistant Director)
  Geological Survey of Great Britain
  Southpark 19, Grange Terrace
  Edinburgh 9, Scotland
Greece
  Service géologique de Grèce
  Rue de l'Académie, 38
  Athens
Hungary
  Orszagos Foldtani Intézet
  (National Geological Institute)
  14, Vorosilov-ut
  Budapest, XIV
India
  Geological Survey of India
  27 Choringhee
  Calcutta 13
Indo-China
  Service géologique de l'Indo-Chine
  Hanoi
Iraq
  Geological Department
  Ministry of Economics
  Baghdad
Ireland
  Geological Survey
  14 Hume Street
  Dublin
Italy
  Ufficio Geologico
  Largo S. Susanna, 13
  Rome
Japan
  Geological Survey of Japan

135 Hisamoto-cho
Kawasaki
Kenya
   Commissioner of Mines
   Mining and Geological Department
   P.O. Box 339
   Nairobi
Luxemburg
   Service géologique de Luxembourg
   38 Boulevard de la Foire
   Luxemburg
Madagascar
   Directeur des mines
   Gouvernement de Madagascar.
   Tananarive
Malayan Union
   Geological Survey
   Batu Gajah
Mexico
   Instituto geologico
   6A del Cipres 176
   Mexico, D.F.
Morocco
   Service géologique
   Division des mines et de la géologie
   Rabat
Netherlands
   Rijks Geologische Dienst
   Haarlem, Spaarne 17
New Zealand
   New Zealand Geological Survey
   156, The Terrace
   Wellington, C.1
Nigeria
   Nigeria Geological Survey Department
   Kaduna Junction
   Nigeria
Norway
   Norges Geologiske Undersokelse
   Josefinegate 34
   Oslo
Nyasaland
   Nyasaland Geological Survey Department
   P. O. Box 27
   Zomba

Pakistan
  Geological Survey of Pakistan
  Karachi
Peru
  Director de Minas y Petroleo
  Ministerio de Fomento
  Lima
Philippines
  Philippine Bureau of Mines
  Manila
Poland
  Panstwowy Instytut Geolgiczny
  (Geological Survey of Poland)
  Rakawiecka Street 4
  Warsaw
Portugal
  Servicos Geologicos de Portugal
  Rua da Academia das Ciencias, 19-2
  Lisbon
Rumania
  Institutul Geologic
  Bucharest
Siam
  Royal Department of Mines
  Bangkok
Sierra Leone
  Sierra Leone Geological Survey Department
  Freetown
Southern Rhodesia
  Geological Survey of Southern Rhodesia
  P. O. Box 366
  Salisbury
Spain
  Instituto Geologico y Minero de Espana
  Rios Rosas No. 9
  Madrid
Swaziland
  Swaziland Geological Survey Department
  P. O. Box 9
  Mbabane
Sweden
  Sveriges Geologiska Undersokning
  Stockholm 50
Switzerland
  Geotechnischen Kommission

Sonneggstrasse 5
Zurich 5
Tanganyika
Tanganyika Geological Division
Department of Lands and Mines
Dodoma
Tunisia
Services de mines, de l'industrie et de l'energie
(Service géologique)
Rue de la Kasbah
Tunis
Turkey
Maden Tetkik ve Arama Enstitusa
Ankara

Turkiye jeolojik hartasi (geologic maps)
Ankara
Union of South Africa
Geological Survey
P. O. Box 401
Pretoria
U.S.S.R.
Ministry of Geology
Moscow
Uruguay
Instituto Geologico del Uruguay
Calle Jalio Herrara y Obes No. 1239
Montevideo
Venezuela
Servicio Technico de Mineria y Geologia
Ministerio de Fomento
Caracas
Yugoslavia
Geologiski Institut
Belgrade

CHAPTER 15

BOOKS

No standardized definition of a book or distinction between a book and a pamphlet being available, this chapter can include only such publications as do not belong in the other chapters of this book. According to the rules of the U.S. Copyright Office, even a single sheet qualifies as a book. The U.S. Post Office Department defines a book as consisting of "24 pages or more, at least 22 of which are printed." The *United States Quarterly Book Review*, prepared by the Library of Congress, defines a book as a "bound volume of 100 or more pages," although a few exceptions as to minimum size are made, especially for poetry and concise tools of reference and research. Other cataloguers have other interpretations.

A large proportion of the publications treated as bulletins in Chaps. 10 to 14 fit into the category of books as far as their physical make-up is concerned, but the manner in which they are issued puts them into a different class, as discussed on page 100. Some of the volumes included under index guides and bibliographies (Chap. 7), abstracts (Chap. 8), and theses (Chap. 17) are also books from a mechanical standpoint, but inasmuch as they perform specialized functions, they are dealt with separately in this book.

Books that have been published in the same style, each book complete in itself but all having some common point of interest, constitute a series.

REVIEW SERIES

Books that survey the literature published during a certain period, either critically or in summary, are called reviews. Groups of such books belong to a review series.

In obtaining orientation in a subject, the usefulness of reviews appearing in review series has been well brought out by Byron A. Soule.[1]

Reviews in geologic subjects in the *Annual Reports on the Progress of Chemistry for 19(—)*, published for the Chemical Society by Gurney & Jackson, London, have appeared according to the following schedule:

Crystallography. 1908, 1917, annually 1919 to 1929, 1931, 1933, annually 1935 to 1942

Geochemistry. 1930, 1932

Mineralogical chemistry. Annually 1904 to 1907, 1909, 1915, 1917, 1921, 1923, 1925, 1927, 1929

[1] Soule, Byron A., "Library Guide for the Chemist," pp. 77–84, McGraw-Hill Book Company, Inc., New York, 1938.

Annual Reviews of Petroleum Geology is published by the Institute of Petroleum, London.

Geologic subjects are ably reviewed in *Geographisches Jahrbuch*, published in Gotha since 1866 in one or two volumes per year (except that single volumes covered the periods 1915 to 1918 and 1919 to 1923). Among the aspects of geology that are included are geophysics, geomorphology, regional geology, and surveying. An extensive key to the contents of this yearbook is given on pages 53 to 57 of "Aids to Geographical Research" by John Kirtland Wright and Elizabeth T. Platt, published by the American Geographical Society, New York (2d ed., 1947).

The progress of mineralogy from 1822 to 1851 was given in *Jahresbericht über die Fortschritte der Chemie und Mineralogie*, published in Tübingen as a translation of Sec. 3 of *Svenska vetenskaps kademien arsberaettelser*. An index was published to Vols. 1 to 25.

REFERENCE BOOKS

Textbooks

There is scant difference between a textbook and any other serious book. Depending upon how intensive or extensive the course is in which it is used, almost any book can serve as a textbook. The appearance or arrangement of certain books, however—especially the presence of secondary (center or side) headings, numbered paragraphs, references, or lists of questions or problems—indicates them to be textbooks rather than scholarly treatises or monographs, which, like textbooks, develop the subject systematically, building upon previously presented material, but which are usually more intensive, more current, and better documented than textbooks. It is when textbooks are used for specific reference purposes rather than for general reading or systematic studying that this chapter is concerned with them. Some of these textbooks are actually bulletins (that is, government documents or the serial publications of institutions) according to the classification adopted in this book.

A list of the best textbooks in general geology (physical or historical) or in any one of the chief branches of geology would be fairly easy to compile and not subject to much dispute. The many suitable textbooks that would be required for an adequate representation of all the phases of geology would make a list too long for inclusion here. Such books will be found listed, described, and evaluated among other books in the book lists, bibliographies of books, and book reviews discussed in this chapter.

Handbooks

Miscellaneous reference data in summary form, including extensive lists and tables, make up the contents of scientific and technical handbooks.

The term handbook is not used here in the sense of the German Handbuchs, which are comprehensive, usually noncritical compilations on an exhaustive scale.

The condensation required for reasons of space necessitates the use of numerous abbreviations and symbols. Furthermore, the utility of most handbook information is restricted to readers already familiar with the terminology of the subject and the conceptions it involves.

The following handbooks all contain information of especial use to geologists and geologic engineers. The handbooks of chemistry include data about the earth, tables of the properties of minerals, and synonyms of mineral names, as well as a wide range of knowledge about chemistry. Only books still published are included.

"Mining Engineers' Handbook," edited by Robert Peele, 3d ed., John Wiley & Sons, Inc., New York, 1941, 2 vols.

"Practical Petroleum Engineers' Handbook" by Joseph Zaba and W. T. Doherty, 3d ed., Gulf Publishing Company, Houston, 1949.

"A Handbook of Petroleum, Asphalt and Natural Gas," Kansas City Testing Laboratory, Kansas City, Mo., 1928.

"Rotary Drilling Handbook" by J. E. Brantly, 4th ed., Petroleum World, Los Angeles, 1948.

"Handbook of Chemistry," edited by Norbert Adolph Lange, 7th ed., Handbook Publishers, Inc., Sandusky, Ohio, 1949.

"Handbook of Chemistry and Physics," edited by Charles D. Hodgman, 31st ed., Chemical Rubber Publishing Company, Cleveland, 1949.

"Van Nostrand's Chemical Annual," edited by J. C. Olsen, 7th issue, D. Van Nostrand Company, Inc., New York, 1934.

"The Chemist's Year Book," edited by E. Hope, John Sherratt and Son, London, 1947; Chemical Publishing Company, Inc., Brooklyn, 1940.

"Chemiker-Taschenbuch," formerly "Chemiker-Kalender," edited by I. Koppel, 58th ed., Verlag Julius Springer, Berlin, 1937.

Tables

Reference books that consist almost exclusively of tables may conveniently be considered separately from handbooks, but they partake of much the same character. The same precaution regarding the frequency of abbreviations and symbols and the cryptic appearance of the data to someone not well grounded in the fundamental principles and terminology involved applies to both types of reference material.

The following books of tables all contain information valuable to geologists.

"Handbook of Physical Constants" by Francis Burch, J. F. Schairer, and H. Cecil Spicer, *Special Publication* 36, Geological Society of America, New York, 1942.

"International Critical Tables of Numerical Data, Physics, Chemistry and Technology," Edward W. Washburn, editor in chief, prepared under the auspices of the International Research Council and the National Academy of Sciences by the National Research Council, McGraw-Hill Book Company, Inc., New York, 1926 to 1933, 7 vols. and index.

"Smithsonian Physical Tables," Frederick E. Fowle, editor, *Publication* 3171 (Vol. 88), 8th ed., Smithsonian Institution, Washington, 1933.

"Zahlenwerte und Funktionen aus Physik, Chemie, Astronomie, Geophysik, Tecknik," formerly "Landolt-Börnstein physicalisch-chemische Tabellen," 6th ed., Verlag Julius Springer, Berlin, 1950.   Vol. 3 is Astrophysik und Geophysik.

"Tables annuelles de constantes et données numériques de chimie, de physique, de biologie et de technologie," Gauthier-Villars & Cie, Paris; University of Chicago Press, Chicago, 1910 to 1932, 10 vols. and 3 indexes.

Yearbooks

Handbooks that are prepared with an emphasis on the inclusion of current material, especially statistics and reviews of recent progress, are known as yearbooks.   Their equivalents in popular reference books are the almanacs.   Their contents pertain largely to technological developments, production figures, and commercial information; the focus of geologic yearbooks is therefore on the mining and petroleum industries.   The following yearbooks are currently published.   Additional books of a similar type that in future years may become yearbooks are enumerated by Blanche H. Dalton.[1]

Mining.

Minerals Yearbook, U. S. Bureau of Mines, Washington, 1947 (1948).   A similar yearbook, *The Mineral Industry, Its Statistics, Technology, and Trade,* was published for the years 1892 to 1940, Vols. 1 to 49, by Scientific Publishing Company, New York (1893 to 1910) and McGraw-Hill Book Company, Inc., New York (1911 to 1941).

Metal Statistics, 43d annual ed., American Metal Market, New York, 1950.

Year Book of the American Bureau of Metal Statistics, 29th annual issue, American Bureau of Metal Statistics, New York, 1949.

Mines Register, successor to *The Mines Handbook* and *The Copper Handbook,* Vol. 23, Mines Register, New York, 1949.

Pit and Quarry Handbook and Directory of the Nonmetallic Minerals Industries, 40th ed., Complete Service Publishing Company, Chicago, 1947.

Saward's Annual (coal industry), 32d ed., Saward's Journal, New York, 1949 (1950).

Canadian Mines Handbook, Northern Miner Press, Toronto, 1948.

[1] Dalton, Blanche H., "Sources of Engineering Information," University of California Press, Berkeley, Calif., 1948, 109 pp.

Canadian Mining Manual, National Business Publications, Ltd., Gardenvale, Quebec, 1948.

The Financial Post Survey of Mines; Canada and Newfoundland, Vol. 24, Maclean-Hunter Publishing Company, Montreal, 1950.

Mining Year Book, 63d annual vol., Walter E. Skinner, London, 1949.

Mineral Industry of the British Empire and Foreign Countries: Statistical Summary, Imperial Institute, London, 1949.

The African Manual on Mining and Industry, edited by T. A. Rushton, 21st ed., Mining and Industrial Publications of Africa, Ltd., London, 1949.

South African Mining and Engineering Year Book, 35th year, South African Mining Journal Syndicate, Ltd., Johannesburg, 1947–1948 (1948).

Petroleum.

Oil and Gas Field Development in United States Year Book, Vol. 20, National Oil Scouts and Landmen's Association, Austin, 1949 (1950).

Petroleum Facts and Figures, 9th ed., American Petroleum Institute, New York, 1950.

Statistics of Oil and Gas Development and Production, 4th ed., American Institute of Mining and Metallurgical Engineers, New York, 1949.

Petroleum Register, 27th ed., Los Angeles, 1949.

Geophysical Directory, Houston, 1948.

Directory of Geophysical and Oil Companies Who Use Geophysical Service, Midwest Oil Register, Tulsa, 1950.

Directory of Refining, Natural Gasoline, and Cycling Plants in the United States, Canada, and Latin America, Midwest Oil Register, Tulsa, 1950.

Oil Directories, Midwest Oil Register, Tulsa: *Rocky Mountain Region and New Mexico, Texas, Oklahoma, California, Kansas, Michigan-Illinois-Indiana-Kentucky, Louisiana-Arkansas-Mississippi-Georgia-Florida*, 1950.

Refining Directory, Midwest Oil Register, Tulsa, 1950.

Pipe Line Directory, Midwest Oil Register, Tulsa, 1950.

Rocky Mountain Petroleum Directory, 6th ed., Petroleum Publishers, Inc., Denver, 1950.

Oil Directory of Canada, Midwest Oil Register, Tulsa, 1950.

Oil Directory of Latin America, Midwest Oil Register, Tulsa, 1950.

Oil and Petroleum Yearbook, Walter E. Skinner, 40th annual vol., London, 1949.

Annual Reviews of Petroleum Geology, Vol. 8, Institute of Petroleum, London, 1946 (1949).

Dictionaries

Good geologic definitions are usually found in the several unabridged dictionaries. Besides giving definitions and the other usual dictionary information as to spelling, pronunciation, and etymology, the unabridged dictionaries often take on, for certain subjects, something of the nature of encyclopedias, having tables and extended classifications. The relative merits of 45 dictionaries in the English language available in 1934 are analyzed in Vol. 5, No. 4 (October 1934, 33 pp.) of *Subscription Books Bulletin*, issued by the American Library Association, Chicago. New dictionaries and revised editions are reviewed in current issues of this quarterly publication. D. Jerome Fisher[1] has stated that the pronunciation of mineral names is best given in "The Century Dictionary." Many gazetteers and related reference works give the meaning of generic and other technical terms used in geography; information about such books is given on pages 74 to 78 of "Aids to Geographical Research" by John Kirtland Wright and Elizabeth T. Platt, 2d ed., American Geographical Society, New York, 1947.

The following books are specialized dictionaries of geologic terms.

"Dictionary of Geological Terms" by C. M. Rice, Edwards Bros., Inc., Ann Arbor, Mich., 1943, 461 pp.

"A Glossary of the Mining and Mineral Industries" by Albert H. Fay, *U. S. Bureau of Mines Bulletin* 95, Superintendent of Documents, Government Printing Office, Washington, D. C., 1920, reprinted 1948, 754 pp.

"Petroleum Dictionary for Office, Field and Factory" by Hollis P. Porter, Gulf Publishing Company, Houston, Tex., 1930, 234 pp.

"Glossary of Current and Common Bituminous Coal Mining Terms," Bituminous Coal Institute, Washington, 1947, 26 pp.

"An Etymological Dictionary of Chemistry and Mineralogy" by Dorothy Bailey and Kenneth C. Bailey, Longmans, Green & Co., Inc., New York; Edward Arnold & Co., London, 1929, 308 pp.

"The Nomenclature of Petrology" by Arthur Holmes, 2d ed., Thomas Murby and Company, London, 1928, 284 pp.

"A Glossary of Scientific Names (Chiefly of Fossil Invertebrates)" by Stuart A. Northrop, University of New Mexico Press, Albuquerque, N. M., 1949, 71 pp.

English–foreign-language geologic dictionaries include the following recommended ones.

"Geology and Allied Sciences" by Walter Huebner, Part 1, German-English, Veritas Press, New York, 1939, 405 pp.

"German-English Geological Terminology" by Arnold Cissarz and William R. Jones, Thomas Murby and Company, London; D. Van Nostrand Company, Inc., New York, 1931, 250 pp.

"A German and English Glossary of Geographical Terms" by Eric Fischer and Francis E. Elliott, American Geographical Society, New York, 1950, 118 pp.

"A French-English Vocabulary in Geology and Physical Geography" by G. M. Davies, Thomas Murby and Company, London; D. Van Nostrand Company, Inc., New York, 1932, 140 pp.

"Diccionario y nomenclatura geologica" (Spanish, German, English) by Her-

---

[1] *Mining and Metallurgy*, Vol. 28, p. 417, 1947.

berto Windhausen, Correo No. 8, Yacimientos Petroliferos, Chubut, Argentina.

"A Concise International Dictionary of Mechanics and Geology" (English, French, German, Spanish) by S. A. Cooper, Cassell & Company, Ltd., London, 1950, 404 pp.

"Dictionary of Spanish, Spanish-American, Portuguese, and Portuguese-American Mining, Metallurgical and Allied Terms" by Edward Halse, 3d ed., Charles Griffin & Co., Ltd., London, 1926, 447 pp.

"Geologische Nomenclator" (Dutch, German, English, French, illustrated), edited by L. Rutten, Geologisch-Mijnbouwkundig Genootschap Voor Nederland en Koloniën, The Hague, Netherlands, 1929, 338 pp.

"English-Russian Geological Dictionary" by U. C. Dushen, U.S.S.R., 1937.

"A Vocabulary of Russian-English and English-Russian Mining Terms and Relative Technical Words" by Chester W. Purington and Gita Toderovich, Charles Griffin & Co., Ltd., London, 1920.

"Mijnbouwkundige Nomenclator" (mining terms in Dutch, French, German, Spanish, English), J. B. Wolters' Uitgevers-Maatschappij, Batavia, 1949, 436 pp.

"Glosario de la industria petrolera" (Spanish-English), Departamento de Petroleo, Mexico City, 1930.

"Vocabulario Inglés-Español de la industria petrolera" (Spanish-English), Departamento de Petroleo, Mexico City, 1939.

"Deutsch-spanisch-französisch-englisches Wörterbuch des Berg- und Hüttenkunde" by Max Venator, A. Twietmeyer, Leipzig, 1897–1905.

"Bergtechnisches Taschenwörterbuch" (English-German), edited by Wilhelm Schulz, Verlag Glückauf, Essen, 1934–1936, 2 vols.

"Glossary of Geographical and Topographical Terms and of Words of Frequent Occurrence in the Composition of Such Terms and of Place-Names" by Alexander Knox, Edward Stanford, London, 1904, 472 pp.

The Army Map Service has issued a series of inexpensive glossaries of geographic terms in English and Arabic, Indochinese, Italian, Japanese, Polish, and Spanish; special lists are also available for maps of the Netherlands East Indies and German maps of Russian areas.

Geologic dictionaries and glossaries of selected terms are found in numerous textbooks and other books. A glossary forms a major part of some books, such as "A Descriptive Petrography of the Igneous Rocks," Vol. 1, by Albert Johannsen (University of Chicago Press, 2d ed., 1939) and "A Handbook of Rocks" by James Furman Kemp (D. Van Nostrand Company, Inc., 5th ed., 1923). Most of the terms are included in the dictionaries already listed, some of which state the sources of their contents. Dictionaries and glossaries included in other books pertaining to the mining industry are listed on page 20 of "Business and Trade Dictionaries," Special Libraries Association, New York, 1934. Brief geographic glossaries in numerous languages are given on pages 52 to 135 of "Foreign Maps" by

E. C. Olson and Agnes Whitmarsh, Harper & Brothers, New York, 1944. Technical dictionaries and specialized glossaries of geographic value are named in the *Geographical Review*, Vol. 30, pp. 331–332, 1940.

Most general scientific and technical dictionaries contain numerous geologic definitions. An extensive list of such books is included in "Foreign Language-English Dictionaries," Library of Congress, Washington, 1942 (Supplement, 1944). The dictionaries are arranged alphabetically by language, first in a general list and then in a specialized list which includes scientific and technical dictionaries. A very useful list of German-English scientific dictionaries and glossaries is given in "German-English Science Dictionary" by Louis De Vries, McGraw-Hill Book Company, Inc., New York (2d ed., 1946, 558 pp.).

Foreign-language scientific and technical dictionaries are a necessary part of the literature of geology. The more useful of them include a large number of nontechnical words that appear frequently in scientific literature and hence serve also as a substitute for a literary dictionary to readers whose knowledge of the foreign language is not too extensive.

Encyclopedias

The usefulness of encyclopedia articles as a starting point for studying a subject—because of their presentation of facts, current hypotheses, and bibliographies—and as condensations or summaries of the information that is known has been emphasized on page 8.

The scope and quality of the standard English-language encyclopedias vary considerably. All such books, including new editions and revised printings, are reviewed currently by the Committee on Subscription Books of the American Library Association in *Subscription Books Bulletin*, published quarterly by the American Library Association, Chicago.

Besides being included with other books in the book reviews and book abstracts described below, reference books, both new and those previously published, are critically evaluated in the issues of *Subscription Books Bulletin*, published quarterly since 1930 by the American Library Association, Chicago. An index is issued in October, and cumulations are issued every 4 years.

BOOK REVIEWS

The long dispute about the merits of favorable book reviews in actually selling books may be avoided here, but the value of adequate book reviews is recognized by everyone who has occasion to select books for reading or purchase. The art of writing a good book review has probably resulted in as many successes and as many failures as the art of writing a good book, to which it is scarcely inferior.

The most accessible place to find reviews of geologic books is in the regular geologic periodicals. Incidentally, one of the simple improvements that such periodicals could offer its readers would be to publish these reviews months earlier than they do. Geologic books are also often reviewed in many of the general scientific periodicals that are listed in the publications described on pages 89 to 93. The "Scientist's Bookshelf" in the *American Scientist*, written by Kirtley F. Mather, has been described by Harlow Shapley[1] as probably the best periodical review of scientific books now available. The book-review sections of newspapers occasionally review geologic books, especially those with a popular appeal; the three leading publications of this kind in the United States are the *New York Times Book Review*, *New York Herald Tribune Weekly Book Review*, and *Chicago Sun Book Week*. Many magazines and newspapers that regularly review books are listed in the annual volumes of *American Booktrade Directory*, published by R. R. Bowker Company, New York.

Book reviews are indexed, along with other literature, in the publications described in Chap. 7.

The following publications are devoted to reviewing books. The length and quality of the reviews vary considerably according to the publication, the reviewer, and the importance of the book.

Technical Book Review Index identifies and quotes from reviews in current scientific, technical, and trade periodicals; it is published monthly except July and August by the Special Libraries Association, New York.

New Technical Books review recent additions to the Reference Department of the New York Public Library; it is compiled and annotated by the Science and Technology Division and published bimonthly by the New York Public Library, New York.

ASLIB Book-List reviews and recommends recently published scientific and technical books; it is issued monthly by the Association of Special Libraries and Information Bureaux, London. The author and title index is cumulated annually.

Reviews in English of scientific and technical books published in France between 1940 and 1948 are given in *French Bibliographical Digest*, published at intervals by the Cultural Division of the French Embassy, New York. Issue No. 4, December 1949, deals with geology, and No. 3, November 1949, covers geography.

United States Quarterly Book Review is published by the Rutgers University Press, New Brunswick, New Jersey. It is prepared by the Library of Congress under the program of the Interdepartmental Commission on Scientific and Cultural Cooperation, and prior to the first number of Vol. 4 (1948) it was published by the Library of Congress. The title until October 1950 was *United States Quarterly Book List*. It is a "highly selec-

[1] *Science*, Vol. 111, p. 132, 1950.

tive bibliography of currently published United States books which are believed to make a contribution to the sum of knowledge and experience." Good reviews are given of books in nine major classifications and a varying number of subheadings. An index of authors and a directory of publishers are included.

Technical books, except the most highly technical ones, are reviewed (among others) in *The Book Review Digest*, published monthly except July and bound annually by the H. W. Wilson Company, New York. The books are entered alphabetically by author and are described non-critically, but digests of critical reviews from newspapers and magazines are given. Cumulations to the publication are issued in August and February. Subject and title indexes are included and cumulated in each issue; a 5-year subject and title index is included in the annuals for 1921, 1926, 1931, 1936, and 1941.

New books are selected, classified, catalogued, and described in *The Booklist: A Guide to Current Books*, published on the 1st and 15th of each month (once in August) by the American Library Association, Chicago. A cumulative index is issued in August.

Section 2 of *Wilson Library Bulletin* contains reviews of selected books. This periodical is issued monthly except July and August by the H. W. Wilson Company, New York.

Books are reviewed and appraised in the following library publications: *Bookmark*, New York State Library, University of the State of New York Press, Albany; *Library Journal*, R. R. Bowker Company, New York; *Library Quarterly*, University of Chicago Press, Chicago.

Book reviews are given in the house organs of several American wholesale book distributors. The book list in *British Book News*, published monthly for the British Council by the National Book League, London, contains reviews of books published in the British Commonwealth and Empire. The books are grouped by subject and classified by the Dewey decimal system. Good reviews of technical books appeared before the Second World War (and may appear again) in the house organs of several German publishers, which were distributed free through book dealers. Especially notable were *Polytechnische Bibliothek* (J. A. Barth, Leipzig), *Chemische Novitäten* (Gustav Fock, Leipzig), and *Bremer Literaturberichte für Technik, Chemie und verwandte Gebiete* (G. A. von Halem, Bremen).

Reference books are critically reviewed and compared in *Subscription Books Bulletin*, described on page 176.

BOOK ABSTRACTS

Most of the abstract journals described in Chap. 8 include abstracts of books. These are often very similar to ordinary book reviews, as they usually indicate the value of the book to readers interested in the subject.

LISTS OF NEW BOOKS

Advance notice of some books is obtained from publishers' announcements in book-trade magazines and from circulars and letters sent to persons on their mailing lists, from advertisements and news items in scientific periodicals, and from personal contact and correspondence.

The book reviews and book abstracts already mentioned are probably the best guides to newly published books. Delays attending the inclusion of certain books, however, and the important and numerous omissions that are bound to occur give value to general lists of new books. Such lists, named below, are usually uncritical and often unclassified, but they are the first place where most persons learn about the existence of most new books.

All books that are copyrighted in the United States are recorded in the *Catalog of Copyright Entries of Books and Other Articles Registered under the Copyright Law*, issued semiannually by the Library of Congress and sold by the Superintendent of Documents, Government Printing Office, Washington. The volume is also obtainable in sections under the abbreviated title *Catalog of Copyright Entries*. Part 1, Group 1 deals with books. Entries are alphabetical by author (or, if anonymous, by title) and include the title, date of copyright, copyright number, and name and town of the publisher. Part 1, Group 2 deals with pamphlets, leaflets, and other publications legally registered as books but not included in Group 1; contributions to newspapers or periodicals, etc.; lectures; sermons; addresses for oral delivery; and maps.

The Cumulative Book Index is a current catalogue of all books published in the United States and Canada. The books are catalogued by author, title, and important subjects. All entries are in one alphabet and include author, title, publisher, price, binding, date of publication, and Library of Congress card number. Books and pamphlets issued by authors, printers, societies and institutions, subscription books and books printed privately, as well as the books of established publishing firms are included. This publication is issued monthly except August, with a bound annual volume in December, by the H. W. Wilson Company, New York. Cumulations are published every 5 years and at more frequent intervals. Volumes to date cover 1928 to 1932, 1933 to 1937 (both out of print), 1938 to 1942, January 1943 to June 1945, July 1945 to December 1946, 1947, January to July 1948, August to December 1948, January to July 1949, August to December 1949, and January to July 1950. This list is the current continuation of the *United States Catalog*. "Books in Print January 1, 1928," one of the national bibliographies described on page 182.

Books too recent for inclusion in the last monthly issue of *The Cumulative Book Index* and announcements of forthcoming books are listed in *Publishers' Weekly*. Pamphlets, most paper-bound books, and books of lesser trade interest are listed in smaller type. This, the leading book-trade journal, is issued weekly by R. R. Bowker Company, New York.

The *Vertical File Service Catalog* is an annotated subject list of pamphlets which is issued monthly except August and cumulated annually (since 1934, biennially 1932 to 1934) by the H. W. Wilson Company, New York. The pamphlets are entered alphabetically according to subject and described fully as to title, size, date, cost (if any), and publisher's name and address. A brief note as to the contents of each and a title index are included.

A comprehensive classified annual list of Canadian books is *The Canadian Catalogue of Books Published in Canada, about Canada, as well as Those Written by Canadians*, which has been compiled yearly since 1921 by the Toronto Public Libraries and issued as an annual supplement to *Ontario Library Review*, published by the Public Libraries Branch, Ontario Department of Education, Toronto. The subject headings include mining, natural history, and science, and there is a separate section for French-language publications.

Quill and Quire is a monthly book-trade periodical having a quarterly supplement called *Cumulative Catalogue*, which is a list of new Canadian books arranged alphabetically by title. It is published by Current Publications, Ltd., Toronto.

The British National Bibliography, begun in January 1950, is a weekly catalogue of all books, with certain minor exceptions, currently published in Great Britain.   It is classified according to the Dewey decimal system. A separate author index is issued every fourth week, and an annual volume at the end of the year. The editorial work is conducted at the British Museum; the publisher is the Council of the British National Bibliography, and the distributor is J. Whitaker and Sons, Ltd., London.

The English Catalogue of Books, published by Publishers' Circular, Ltd., Beckenham, Kent, is an annual list of current British and Irish books, arranged alphabetically by author and title.

The same lists, appearing weekly and cumulated in the last issue of each month, are given in *Publishers' Circular and Booksellers' Record*.

All books published in the British Empire during the quarter are listed in *Whitaker's Cumulative Book List*, published by J. Whitaker and Sons, Ltd., London.   The books are listed in two ways—alphabetically by author and title and in a separate classified list of 49 subjects, including one devoted to Geology, mineralogy, and mining. This publication is issued quarterly and cumulated throughout the year, the last number being an annual volume.   Longer cumulations have been issued in author and title but not subject form to cover 1939 to 1943 and 1944 to 1947.

The current subject list in *Whitaker's Cumulative Book List* also appears at monthly intervals in *Current Literature*, likewise published by J. Whitaker and Sons, Ltd., London.

The current author and title list in *Whitaker's Cumulative Book List* also appears at weekly intervals in *The Bookseller*, published by the same firm. The last issue of the month has a monthly list.

In the odd-numbered issues of *Lea*, published monthly since January 1949 by the Columbus Memorial Library of the Pan-American Union, Washington, appears a current bibliography of books published in Latin America. Lists of the bibliographies of the current books of individual Latin American countries are given on pages 11 to 13 of *The Library of Congress Quarterly Journal of Current Acquisitions*, Vol. 7, No. 2, February 1950.

The tragic and confused story of European publishing in scientific and technical books during the Second World War is now being told. Important notes on its war and postwar status are given by Charles Harvey Brown in "Scientific Publishing in Continental Europe," *Science*, Vol. 106, pp. 54–58, July 18, 1947.

Wartime reprints of German books are listed in "Book Republication Program," issued by the former Office of Alien Property Custodian, Washington. They are arranged alphabetically by author with the licensed publishers from whom they can be purchased. Catalog No. 8 (October 1948), obtainable free from J. W. Edwards, Ann Arbor, Michigan, lists about 700 foreign scientific and technical books and sets reproduced by license of the Office of Alien Property, including about 300 books published in Germany since 1941; about half a dozen of the books deal with geology. Copies of the periodicals *Halbjahresverzeichnis* for the years 1941 to 1943 and *Deutsche Nationalbibliographie* for 1944, which listed scientific books published in Germany during those years, have been reproduced photographically by J. W. Edwards, Ann Arbor. In February 1947 Stechert-Hafner, Inc., New York, became the first American firm to send a representative to Germany to purchase and ship current German books. Schoenhof's Foreign Books, Inc., Cambridge, Massachusetts, is another firm specializing in the importation of such books; the names of other companies, from which lists of these books may be obtained, are given from time to time in *Publishers' Weekly* and other book trade magazines and library journals.

Duplication due to the postwar confusion is shown in the simultaneous publication of *Bibliographie der deutschen Bibliothek*, which includes to a considerable extent the material contained in *Deutsche Nationalbibliographie*.[1]

---

[1] Brown, Charles Harvey, Scientific Publishing in Continental Europe, *Science*, Vol. 106, p. 55, 1947.

A record of the books published in Russian (both within and outside the Soviet Union) and currently received by the Library of Congress and cooperating libraries is given in Part A of *Monthly List of Russian Accessions*, published since April 1948 by the Library of Congress, Washington. Books published since 1945 are classified by subject, including Geology and Geography.

Lists of current books in other countries throughout the world are given in the sources enumerated in "Current National Bibliographies" by Parker Worley, published in *The Library of Congress Quarterly Journal of Current Acquisitions*, beginning with Vol. 6, No. 4, August 1949. This series of catalogues is the contribution of the Library of Congress to the production of comprehensive current national bibliographies as recommended by the Conference on International Cultural, Educational, and Scientific Exchanges held at Princeton University in November 1946. The above lists are a revision and expansion of "Current National Bibliographies: A List of Sources of Information Concerning Current Books of All Countries" by Lawrence Heyl, published in 1942 in Chicago by the American Library Association (rev. ed., 19 pp.); this mimeographed list was confined principally to sources of information concerning publications in the book trade.

In searching for entries of foreign books, those from Latin America may often be found as a group instead of being listed by country. Similarly, books in Slavic languages, though from various countries, may be grouped under Slavic; books in the Arabic language may be grouped under Arabic or, together with books in other languages, may be entered under East, Far East, or Near East; the Indian states are sometimes listed separately, and sometimes their books appear under India or British India.[1]

To learn of current books in some foreign countries where no national bibliographies exist, one must read periodicals having good book reviews and lists of new books and obtain the catalogues of certain book dealers who specialize in such books; the names of these dealers appear on occasion in *Publishers' Weekly*, other book-trade journals, and publications devoted to the library profession.

LISTS OF SELECTED BOOKS

Selected lists, of various lengths, of the most highly recommended books on geology, its branches, special fields, and related sciences may be found in standard textbooks. More comprehensive specialized lists are found in special books and geologic monographs. The best of the regularly published books (textbooks or otherwise) on any geologic subject may offer the most satisfactory approach to a geologic problem, and indeed, because

[1] Heyl, Lawrence, "Current National Bibliographies," p. 1, American Library Association, Chicago, 1942.

of their lists of references, their use may be the preferred way to begin a survey of the literature. Nevertheless, a listing of such books does not seem necessary in the present book, partly for the same consideration of space that justifies omitting specific names of useful periodicals in favor of the index guides that list such periodicals, as in Chap. 9. The catalogues of the leading publishers of scientific books should be consulted and can be secured regularly by having one's name placed on the publishers' mailing lists. A compilation of the current catalogues of the principal publishers, arranged alphabetically and bound into a book, is available in the United States as *Publishers' Trade List Annual*, R. R. Bowker Company, New York (78th ed., 2 vols., 1950). An author and title index to the 1950 edition is published under the title *Books in Print, 1950*.

Lists of selected geologic books are also given in the following places.

A list of 83 leading books dealing with various phases of geology, predominately petroleum geology, is given on pages 1327 to 1330 of the "Directory of Geological Material in North America," by J. V. Howell and A. I. Levorsen, published in Vol. 30, No. 8, Pt. 2, of *Bulletin of the American Association of Petroleum Geologists*, August 1946. These books are listed under the following headings: Dictionaries, glossaries, encyclopedias, statistics, etc.; Miscellaneous; Petroleum production and engineering; Petroleum geology, textbooks, field methods, field descriptions; Miscellaneous (oil industry); Geophysical prospecting; Mineral resources and economics (including petroleum).

A carefully selected list of about 6,000 recent American books constitutes the volume titled "Scientific, Medical, and Technical Books Published in the United States of America 1930–1944: A Selected List of Titles in Print with Annotations." Looking through the sections on Geology, Physics, Chemistry, Mining engineering, Metallurgy, and Military science reveals many books of importance to geologists. This book was edited by R. R. Hawkins, sponsored by the National Research Council's Committee on Bibliography of American Scientific and Technical Books, and published in 1946 in Washington. It was financed by voluntary contributions from publishers and by the purchase of 5,000 copies by the Department of State for distribution abroad. The latter service has proved so useful that a "Supplement. 1945–1948" was published in 1950 by R. R. Bowker Company, New York, adding 2,600 new titles in its 514 pages.

A similar, but much smaller, British volume is "Select List of Standard British Scientific and Technical Books," compiled at the request of the British Council and published (3d ed., 1946, 63 pp.) by the Association of Special Libraries and Information Bureaux, London. Among the subjects are Geology and geophysics, Mineralogy, and Mining, each being subdivided further.

LISTS OF OLDER BOOKS

A complete list of books published since the earliest date or during any given period has never been compiled and is never likely to be. The Project of Bibliographical Control of the United Nations Educational Scientific and Cultural Organization (UNESCO) is the beginning of an international attempt to compile all the sources that will together give this information, which is, of course, not available in any single publication. This information is easier to obtain for the twentieth century than for others and for English than for other languages.

The card indexes and printed catalogues of books of certain important libraries—those of universities, organizations, and national and other large public libraries—would collectively make a fairly comprehensive list of the books that have been published.

National bibliographies, which register the books published in each country, and other catalogues of books previously published are enumerated and described in "National Bibliographies" by Robert Alexander Peddie (Grafton & Company, London, 1912); in "Selected National Bibliographies" (*New York State Library School Bulletin* 38, 1915); and in the standard reference books in the following list.

"A World Bibliography of Bibliographies" by Theodore Besterman, published by the author, London, distributed by the H. W. Wilson Company, New York, Vol. 1, *A* to *L*, 1939; Vol. 2, *M* to *Z*, 1940; 2d ed., Vol. 1, *A* to *H*, 1947.

"Register of National Bibliography" by William P. Courtney, Constable & Co., Ltd., London, 1905–1912, 3 vols.

"Reference Books" by John Minto, The Library Association, London, 1929; Supplement, 1931.

"Guide to Reference Books" by Isadore Gilbert Mudge, 6th ed., American Library Association, Chicago, 1936. Supplemented by "Reference Books of 19... to 19... " by Constance M. Winchell, Vol. 4, 1944–1946 (1947).

"Bibliography: Practical, Enumerative, Historical" by Harry B. Van Hoesen and Frank K. Walter, Charles Scribner's Sons, New York, 1929.

"Internationale Bibliographie der Bibliographien" by Hanns Bohatta and Walter Funke, Vittorio Klostermann, Frankfurt, 1939–1950, 8 parts.

"Handbuch der Bibliographie" by Georg Schneider, Verlag Karl W. Hiersemann, Leipzig, 1930.

"Manuel de bibliographie générale" by Henri Stein, Alphonse Picard et Fils, Paris, 1897.

Many of the national bibliographies and other directories recorded in the above books are arranged or indexed by subjects, including geology and related entries. The following catalogues, however, are devoted to geologic publications of past years.

"Bibliographia zoologiae et geologiae: A General Catalogue of All Books, Tracts, and Memoirs on Zoology and Geology" by Louis Agassiz, corrected, enlarged, and edited by H. W. Strickland, published in 4 vols. by the Ray Society, 1848 to 1854.

"The Geological Record: An Account of Works on Geology, Mineralogy, and Paleontology Published during the Year...." It covers 1874 to 1884.

"Bibliographia geologica" by Michel Mourlon. Published in Brussels, Belgium. Series *A*, in 9 parts, deals with publications before 1896; Series *B*, in 7 parts, deals with those since 1896.

CHAPTER 16

NEWSPAPERS

Much current information of geologic interest, usually technological or biographical but often strictly scientific, appears only in newspapers. Sometimes the information is a preliminary announcement of research which appears to the editor to have news value but which may never be carried far enough to completion to reach a more permanent publication. More often the information is a recent discovery or a new interpretation of data which may not be published as an article in a periodical for a considerable length of time. Many newspaper stories, of course, represent popularizations (too often inaccurate) of material already published or just presented at a scientific meeting and hence ready for publication, at least in abstract form. Other items are of little or no value at all.

The only currently published newspaper index is *The New York Times Index*. Beginning February 1948 it has been issued semimonthly, on the 6th and 21st, to cover the first and second halves, respectively, of the preceding month's contents of *The New York Times*. From 1930 to 1947 it appeared monthly; from 1913 to 1929, quarterly. It has been cumulated annually since 1930.

Many newspapers maintain unpublished indexes of their own, some on a general basis and others for local and regional material only. Some of these indexes are on cards, and some are in loose-leaf or bound (but unpublished) volumes. They can be consulted at the newspaper offices.

A chronological table of American newspaper indexes is given on page 243 of "Newspaper Indexing" by Harry A. Freeman, published in 1942 by the Marquette University Press, Milwaukee. This table gives the name of the newspaper or other sponsor (such as a library, cooperative enterprise, business firm, or the government), the date started, and the period covered. News items since 1728 can be located through the use of these indexes. A survey of the history and range of the indexes is contained in Chap. 2 (pages 8 to 19) of the book mentioned above.

Some of the indexes to newspapers published between 1728 and 1940, compiled by the Works Progress Administration, have been printed or processed and can be consulted at certain libraries. The location of files of these newspapers for the years 1821 to 1936 is given in "American Newspapers 1821–1936: A Union List of Files Available in the United States and Canada," edited by Winifred Gregory under the auspices of the Bibliographical Society of America and published in 1937 by the H. W. Wilson Company, New York.

The same information for American newspapers for the years 1690 to 1820 is given in the "History and Bibliography of American Newspapers, 1690–1820," by Clarence S. Brigham, published in two volumes in 1947 by the American Antiquarian Society, Worcester, Massachusetts.

Augmenting (by either name or date) these lists of newspaper files to the year 1945 but not duplicating them is "Local Indexes in American Libraries," edited by Norma O. Ireland and published in 1945 by the F. W. Faxon Company, Boston.

The Union Catalog Division of the Library of Congress, Washington, maintains a master card catalogue of newspapers (in many languages) on microfilm. It was published in 1948 by the Association of Research Libraries as "Newspapers on Microfilm: A Union Check List" by George A. Schwegmann, Jr. This will be kept up to date by entries in "Union List of Microfilms," which is described in Chap. 6. At intervals the Library of Congress issues mimeographed lists of special categories of newspapers available on microfilm; some are foreign newspapers, foreign-language newspapers published in the United States, labor newspapers, etc.

Published lists of newspapers in practically all countries of the world are given in the sources enumerated in "Current National Bibliographies" by Parker Worley, published in *The Library of Congress Quarterly Journal*, beginning with Vol. 6, No. 4, August 1949 (see page 182).

CHAPTER 17

THESES

Theses or dissertations are partial requirements in most colleges and universities for advanced (master's and doctor's) degrees. Most theses are accepted in typewritten form, with two, three, or four copies that are usually bound and distributed among various libraries and offices of the school. Such theses must generally be consulted at the school; part or all of the thesis may sometimes be copied by one of the photographic methods of reproduction discussed in Chap. 6; an interlibrary loan may sometimes be secured, as discussed in the same chapter.

Some schools require that the thesis be printed and a certain number of copies deposited in the library. An occasional thesis is published in full, listed in the same trade bibliographies as the other books described in Chap. 15, and sold in the same stores. A thesis may also be published in a periodical (Chap. 9) or bulletin (Chaps. 10 to 14), and a stated number of copies of the separates or reprints supplied to the institution. Either the original copies or the separates or reprints are usually available by exchange or purchase, or they can be consulted (or borrowed) at a library, especially a college or university library, that has obtained them in one of these ways. When the thesis is too long to be printed in full, the complete text may be obtained only from the original thesis itself or from a photographic reproduction of it.

Some theses are abstracted in the abstract journals (Chap. 8), even though not otherwise put into print; for example, theses are listed fifth among the entries within certain sections of *Chemical Abstracts*. A more likely but less convenient place to find abstracts of theses is in bulletins of the educational institution sponsoring the research; some of the larger schools devote a separate issue at certain intervals to the presentation of such abstracts.

University Microfilms, Ann Arbor, Michigan, publishes semiannually its *Microfilm Abstracts*, a compilation of abstracts of doctoral theses the full text of which can be purchased in microfilm. (Beginning with Vol. 6, No. 2, abstracts of longer monographs were included in addition to theses.) Each issue contains a cumulative index of titles abstracted in preceding issues. In addition to microfilm, 6- by 8-inch enlargements on paper are available. This firm now issues in this way more than 10 per cent of the doctoral theses written each year in the United States.

All available lists of theses titles and collections of abstracts are believed to be included in "Guide to Bibliographies of Theses" by Thomas R.

Palfrey and Henry E. Coleman, Jr., published in 1940 by the H. W. Wilson Company, New York. An earlier edition was published in 1936 by the American Library Association. The book consists of three parts: (1) general lists of theses without regard to subject; (2) lists in various fields according to subject; (3) institutional lists, giving a bibliography of publications issued by universities (arranged alphabetically) that have listed their own theses.

Lists of published theses

Section 8 of "A Select Bibliography of Chemistry, 1492–1897, First Supplement," by Henry Carrington Bolton, is a catalogue of theses published independently from 1492 to 1897, compiled from material in the Library of Congress, the library of the U.S. Geological Survey, the Strassburg University Library, and other sources. This bibliography is *Publication* 1253, which is Vol. 1, Art. 3 of *Smithsonian Miscellaneous Collections*, published in 1901 by the Smithsonian Institution, Washington. "A Select Bibliography of Chemistry, 1492–1902, Second Supplement," brought the list to the end of 1902. Section 8, "Academic Dissertations," appears on pages 230 to 396 of *Publication* 1440, which is part of Vol. 44 of *Smithsonian Miscellaneous Collections*, published in 1904; it was also published separately in 1901.

The Library of Congress, Washington, published from 1913 to 1939 an annual *List of American Doctoral Dissertations Printed in 19...*, covering the years 1912 to 1938. Only printed theses received in the Catalog Division of the Library of Congress were included. Some volumes are still in print and are sold by the Superintendent of Documents (see page 104).

Lists of accepted theses

United States. The National Research Council of the National Academy of Sciences published lists of doctorates conferred in American universities, with the titles arranged by subjects, from 1920 to 1933. A catalogue of these lists, which were published in the Reprint and Circular Series, is given below.

No. 12. *Doctorates Conferred in the Sciences in 1920 by American Universities.* Compiled by Callie Hull, November 1920, 9 pp.

No. 26. *Doctorates Conferred in the Sciences by American Universities in 1921.* Compiled by Callie Hull and Clarence J. West, March 1922, 20 pp.

No. 42. *Doctorates Conferred in the Arts and Sciences by American Universities, 1921–1922.* Compiled by Clarence J. West and Callie Hull, March 1923, 14 pp.

No. 75. *Doctorates Conferred in the Sciences by American Universities, 1925–1926.* Compiled by Callie Hull and Clarence J. West, March 1927, 34 pp.

No. 80. *Doctorates Conferred in the Sciences by American Universities, 1926–1927.*
Compiled by Callie Hull and Clarence J. West, November 1927, 36 pp.

No. 86. *Doctorates Conferred in the Sciences by American Universities, 1927–1928.*
Compiled by Callie Hull and Clarence J. West, October 1928, 38 pp.

No. 91. *Doctorates Conferred in the Sciences by American Universities, 1928–1929.*
Compiled by Callie Hull and Clarence J. West, September 1929, 46 pp.

No. 95. *Doctorates Conferred in the Sciences by American Universities, 1929–1930.*
Compiled by Callie Hull and Clarence J. West, September 1930, 49 pp.

No. 101. *Doctorates Conferred in the Sciences by American Universities, 1930–1931.*
Compiled by Callie Hull and Clarence J. West, September 1931, 55 pp.

No. 104. *Doctorates Conferred in the Sciences by American Universities, 1931–1932.*
Compiled by Callie Hull and Clarence J. West, October 1932, 59 pp.

No. 105. *Doctorates Conferred in the Sciences by American Universities, 1932–1933.*
Compiled by Callie Hull and Clarence J. West, August 1933, 63 pp.

Since 1934 lists have been prepared by the Association of Research Libraries and published annually under the title *Doctoral Dissertations Accepted by American Universities* by the H. W. Wilson Company, New York. There are at present 16 volumes in the series, as follows:

No. 1, 1933 to 1934, 98 pp.
No. 2, 1934 to 1935, 102 pp.
No. 3, 1935 to 1936, 102 pp.
No. 4, 1936 to 1937, 105 pp.
No. 5, 1937 to 1938, 109 pp.
No. 6, 1938 to 1939, 113 pp.
No. 7, 1939 to 1940, 126 pp.
No. 8, 1940 to 1941, 142 pp.
No. 9, 1941 to 1942, 128 pp.
No. 10, 1942 to 1943, 110 pp.
No. 11, 1943 to 1944, 88 pp.
No. 12, 1944 to 1945, 68 pp.
No. 13, 1945 to 1946, 71 pp.
No. 14, 1946 to 1947, 100 pp.
No. 15, 1947 to 1948, 137 pp.
No. 16, 1948 to 1949, 176 pp.

Theses are listed according to subject and then subdivided by school; there is an alphabetical subject index with cross references. A list of educational institutions indicates how the theses are published and preserved, including whether printing is required, whether microfilming is accepted, whether abstracts are published, how many manuscript copies are supplied to the library, and whether typed or printed copies are loaned. There is also a list of university periodicals abstracting dissertations.

An occasional specialized list has been published by the National Research Council in outside scientific periodicals. These lists are indexed under "theses" or "dissertations" in such periodicals and in abstracts, bibliographies, or indexes prepared from them.

Lists of doctoral theses in geography accepted in the United States are published at intervals in *Annals of the Association of American Geographers* (Vol. 25, pp. 211–237, 1935; Vol. 36, pp. 215–247, 1946).

The following publications contain lists of foreign theses in several important European countries.

Germany. Jahres-Verzeichnes der an den deutschen Universitäten erschienenen Schriften includes the theses of all German universities since 1885, of the Technische Hochschulen since 1913, and of the Hochschulen der Länder since 1924. Most of the volumes are classified by institution and have a subject index and an author index. This publication was published annually in Berlin since 1887 by Asher, Behrend, or Behrend & Ges.

France. Catalogue de thèses et écrits académiques includes the theses of French universitites since 1884. It is classified variously by subject (*faculté*) and institution (prior to 1914) and has annual author indexes and 5-year author and subject indexes. It is issued annually by the Ministère de l'instruction publique and has been published in Paris by Hachette and by Leroux.

Switzerland. Jahresverzeichnis der schweizerischen Hochschulschriften or *Catalogue des écrits académiques suisses* has been published (under various titles) annually since 1897 in Basel by Verlag der Universitätsbibliothek or Schweighauserische Buchdruckerei. It is classified by institution and has an author index; a subject index was published separately in 1927 to cover 1897 to 1923.

Partial lists of foreign theses, including those sponsored by special classes of educational institutions, are given on pages 28 to 33 of "Guide to Reference Books" by Isadore Gilbert Mudge, published by the American Library Association, Chicago (6th ed., 1936).

CHAPTER 18

UNPUBLISHED MANUSCRIPTS

The solution to the problem of locating the unpublished results of research is largely a matter of extensive miscellaneous reading and wide personal contacts. The publication by title only of a scientific article (whether completed or not) in scientific periodicals (Chap. 9) or in the proceedings of scientific organizations (Chap. 11) will often give the information as to author and institution necessary to locate the original article before it is published or the original material before it is prepared for publication. Such titles or the abstracts of papers presented but not yet published are often recorded in the abstract journals (Chap. 8). The delivery of lectures, addresses, and other talks of geologic interest is sometimes reported in the news columns of scientific periodicals, such as *Science*, as well as in newspapers (Chap. 17). When the entire contents of a lecture or address are published, the abstract and title may be expected to appear in the abstract journals (Chap. 8) and index guides (Chap. 7) in the same way as regular published material.

With the increasing necessity of limiting the length of published scientific articles—for reasons of cost, space, prompt publication, and general interest—detailed results of much geologic research may not be published; this is especially true of theses (Chap. 17). Such missing details may prove to be indispensable to certain other geologists, who can then scarcely regard the original paper as other than unpublished material.

A number of plans have been proposed to provide for the recording and dissemination to interested scientists of the complete contents of long research papers. An enterprise of this kind is the auxiliary publication program established in 1937 by the American Documentation Institute. Besides its translation services (see page 48) and its microfilming and photoprinting of series of scientific and scholarly periodicals (see page 46), the Institute sells microfilm and photoprint reproductions of papers deposited with it by 88 participating periodicals and institutions. Some of these papers were unpublished, but more have been published in part or by title. About 2,000 items had been deposited to Oct. 15, 1946. The laboratories of the Institute are situated by cooperative agreement in the Library of the U.S. Department of Agriculture, which uses the same facilities for its Bibliofilm Service. The microfilms are 35 mm, and the photoprints are 6 by 8 inches. The price of the latter is usually very expensive. Delivery time is about 10 days. Orders with remittance should be sent to the American Documentation Institute, Washington. The

"Catalog of Auxiliary Publications" indexed by subject (Geology, pp. 20–21) can be obtained free upon request.

The "List of Manuscript Bibliographies in Geology and Geography" by Homer P. Little; the "List of Manuscript Bibliographies in Chemistry and Chemical Technology" by Clarence J. West and Callie Hull; and the "List of Manuscript Bibliographies in Astronomy, Mathematics, and Physics" by Clarence J. West and Callie Hull are described in Chap. 7 on bibliographies.

In December 1930 the Colorado State Planning Commission, Denver, issued in processed form the "Annotated Catalogue of Unpublished Engineering and Geological Reports on Mineral Resources of Colorado," which was complied by the Works Progress Administration. It can be consulted at various libraries.

Various guides to manuscript collections, some of them indexed, have been published by large libraries, including the Library of Congress, and other repositories collecting and preserving manuscripts, such as the National Archives.[1] There seems to be no available list of such guides.

The unpublished manuscript and map material in the library of the Instituto de Geologia de Mexico is reported to be of considerable geologic value.[2]

Personal contact by correspondence or otherwise is necessary to secure information about the continuing results of research which has not been announced, of completed but not yet published material, or of much commercial and industrial research. The increasing tendency in the petroleum industry to exchange stratigraphic data freely is indicative of the trend toward sharing knowledge for the common benefit.

An analysis of unpublished research in geologic science, primarily in North America, is being undertaken by the American Geological Institute, which is planning to compile this information annually or biennially.[3]

[1] "Guide to the Records in the National Archives," *Nat. Archives Pub.* 49-13, Government Printing Office, Washington, D. C., 1948.

[2] Howell, J. V., and A. I. Levorsen, Directory of Geological Material in North America, *Am. Assoc. Petroleum Geologists Bull.*, Vol. 30, No. 8, Pt. 2, p. 1348, 1946.

[3] *Science*, Vol. 110, p. 597, 1949.

CHAPTER 19

MAPS

That maps are an integral part of geologic literature is often not recognized so readily as it should be. Perhaps the necessity for storing maps apart from conventional printed matter is responsible; probably the difficulties inherent in classifying and cataloguing maps add to the failure to consider them in the same light as books and other publications. Every geologist and student of geology knows, nevertheless, that maps are a vital form of geologic literature and need to be used at all times in close conjunction with the other types of literature.

The kinds of maps are so numerous and the terminology of cartography and photogrammetry is so complex that map classification is no easy task. It is, moreover, beyond the scope of this book. Even the chief kinds of maps of value to geologists, though grouped for convenience as outline maps, topographic maps, geologic maps, etc., include a rich variety of specific types. Among the histories of cartography, one of especial interest to geologists is an article by H. A. Ireland, "History of the Development of Geologic Maps," published in the *Bulletin of the Geological Society of America*, Vol. 54, pp. 1227–1280, 1943. The classification and cataloguing of maps and the problems involved are discussed in Chap. 17 of "Official Map Publications" by Walter Thiele (American Library Association, Chicago, 1938) and in the references cited in the footnotes to that chapter. A subject classification of maps is given in Appendix 1 (pp. 297–308 of the same book). The Special Libraries Association, New York, published in 1945 "Classification and Cataloging of Maps and Atlases" by S. W. Boggs and Dorothy C. Lewis (175 pp.). Another useful book of this kind is "Manual for the Classification and Cataloguing of Maps in the Society's Collection," published in 1947 by the American Geographical Society, New York (Mimeographed and Offset Publication No. 4, 43 pp.).

A complete directory of map sources would be almost as voluminous as a list of publishers of periodicals, books, or any of the other types of geologic literature discussed in this book. It would likely be even more difficult to prepare.

Locating maps for use in a particular geologic investigation is complicated by their publication in periodicals (including reprints), bulletins, and books and in collections of maps called atlases, as well as individually. For example, one-half to three-quarters of the maps catalogued by the American Geographical Society are in periodicals and books.[1] "The Cata-

[1] Platt, Elizabeth T., The Map Department of the American Geographical Society, *Public Documents*, 1934, p. 119.

logue of Small-Scale Geological Maps Useful for Broader Regional Studies,"
by Walter H. Bucher and others, published (mineographed) in 1933 by
the Division of Geology and Geography of the National Research Council,
Washington, can be of service in finding such maps.

Many of the important guides to the international geologic, including
geographic, literature described in this book contain entries, often under
Geologic maps, for new maps along with the other types of publications.
These include especially the *Bibliography of North American Geology* (see
page 57), *Bibliography and Index of Geology Exclusive of North America*
(see page 57), and *Annotated Bibliography of Economic Geology* (see page
71).

Part 1, Group 2, of *Catalog of Copyright Entries* (see page 179) includes
all maps copyrighted in the United States during the period covered.
These maps, as well as a great quantity of others, are deposited in the
Division of Maps of the Library of Congress, Washington, which is present-
ly acquiring over 100,000 maps and atlases yearly.[1]

The bibliographic aids in "Official Map Publications" (see page 196 of
this chapter), "Foreign Maps" (see page 196), and "Aids to Geographical
Research" (see below); the indexes to government documents described
in Chap. 10, especially "Publications of the Geological Survey" (see page
113) and Price List 53 of the Superintendent of Documents (see page 105);
and the guides to state and county publications described in Chaps. 12
and 13, respectively, will particularly facilitate the finding of other wanted
maps of specific parts of the United States.

References to foreign map indexes and catalogues are given in the indexes
to foreign-government documents described in Chap. 14 of this book; in
Chaps. 12 to 16 of "Official Map Publications"; on pp. 223–230 of "Foreign
Maps"; and in "Aids to Geographical Research" (especially pp. 83–91)
by John Kirtland Wright and Elizabeth T. Platt, 2d ed., published in 1947
as *Research Series* 22 by the American Geographical Society, New York.
The last book includes a useful guide to map bibliography and is well
indexed.

Various libraries, especially the Library of Congress, Washington, have
published catalogues of the maps and atlases in their holdings. The
maps stored in the National Archives, including those of the U. S. Geological Survey, are indexed in "Your Government's Records in the National
Archives," *Publication* 46–18, 1947 (available free from the National Archives, Washington), and they are described in "Guide to the Records in
the National Archives," *Publication* 49-13, 1948 (sold by the Superintendent of Documents, see page 104).

A valuable feature of "Directory of Geological Material in North America"

[1] *Library of Cong. Quart. Jour. of Current Acquisitions*, Vol. 4, p. 55, 1947.

(see page 208) is the detailed information about kinds and sources of maps given for each state and territory of the United States, each province of Canada, Newfoundland, Mexico, and the Central American countries. This is the most complete, convenient, and up-to-date (1947) catalogue of all kinds of maps most useful to the geologist available in a single publication.

UNITED STATES GOVERNMENT MAPS

"Official Map Publications" by Walter Thiele, published by American Library Association, Chicago (planographed, 356 pp.), is a comprehensive catalogue, to 1938, of public agencies that issue maps in the United States and several other countries. It is a bibliographic guide to such maps and the mapping services and distributing agencies responsible for them. Following a general historical study of cartography, the book discusses the mapping functions and activities of the United States government and gives a reference list of the map publications of its various agencies, together with a parallel column of bibliographic aids which name the catalogues, price lists, and index guides that identify and describe the maps. The arrangement is alphabetical according to department, agency, and map subject or title.

A more recent (1944) book of similar content, less detailed but more comprehensive, is "Foreign Maps" by Everett C. Olson and Agnes Whitmarsh, published in Harper's Geoscience Series by Harper & Brothers, New York (254 pp.). An important section deals with the principal map series of the United States, and there is information on catalogues and lists pertaining to them.

To give a similar discussion here would necessitate virtually repeating the same data, though bringing it more up to date. This later information about maps published by these agencies, most of which are in Washington, can best be secured by writing to the agencies concerned and by examining the entries of new publications in the various catalogues of government publications described in Chap. 10 of this book.

Price List 53, obtainable free from the Superintendent of Documents (see page 105), is a catalogue of most of the important government maps that are sold by that office.

A brief outline of United States government maps, especially those most useful to geologists and specifically mineral collectors, is given on pages 281 to 287 of "Mineral Collectors Handbook" by Richard M. Pearl, Mineral Book Company, Colorado Springs (1947, 297 pp.).

Geological Survey

The following important maps are published by the U.S. Geological Survey. Geologic and economic geology maps of the United States and

various regions within it are discussed first, followed by national and regional topographic maps and base maps and then maps of the individual
states.

Geologic Map of the United States was published in 1933 in four sheets,
each 27 by 47 inches, which may be trimmed and pasted to make a single
wall map 51 by 90 inches, on a scale of 1:2,500,000. More than 160 rock
units are distinguished by patterns printed in 23 colors.

Mineral-resources Maps of the United States include *Coal Fields of the
United States*, published in 1942 in two sheets, 56 by 85 inches, on a scale
of 1:2,500,000; *Oil and Gas Fields of the United States*, showing oil and gas
fields, refining centers, and pipe lines, published in 1946 in two sheets, 52 by
81 inches, on a scale of 1:2,500,000.

Missouri Basin Studies Maps are regional and state mineral-resources
maps issued as the result of geologic mapping and mineral-resource investigations conducted by the Geological Survey as a part of the program
of the Department of the Interior for the study and development of the
Missouri River Basin. The 22 maps issued to the beginning of 1950
include two regional maps.

Tennessee River Basin Maps include a mineral-resources map of parts
of nine states, on a scale of 1:500,000.

Oil and Gas Preliminary Maps are the result of a program of regional
geologic studies initiated July 1, 1943, to examine the possibilities of dis-
covering new supplies of petroleum and natural gas. A total of 109 maps,
reproduced by photolithography, were published to the beginning of 1950.
Thirty-five preliminary charts of various kinds were also issued.

Coal Preliminary Maps have been published for parts of the United
States; seven were issued to the beginning of 1950.

Geophysical Investigations Preliminary Maps are those for which the
data were obtained through the use of the air-borne magnetometer. Iso-
gams (magnetic contours) showing total magnetic intensity are overprinted
on sheets showing geologic or cultural features, thus facilitating the location and correlation of the anomalies with ground features. Thirteen
were issued to the beginning of 1950.

Miscellaneous geologic maps, most of them of oil and gas fields, and
strategic-minerals maps are also published by the Geological Survey.

Some of the topographic quadrangles described below (page 198) are
represented by Folios of the Geologic Atlas of the United States, published
from 1894 to 1945, which contain areal and structural geologic maps and
topographic maps, descriptive text, and illustrations. Additional maps
showing economic geology, oil and gas deposits, and artesian water are included where warranted. The folios measure 18½ by 22 inches; some published for field use are 6 by 9 inches, the maps being folded into a pocket.
A total of 227 were published, of which 24 are in print.

Superseding the Folios of the Geologic Atlas is the new series Geologic Quadrangle Maps of the United States. Besides the geologic maps of selected quadrangles, this series includes structure sections, columnar sections, and the explanatory text required to make the maps useful for general scientific, economic, and engineering purposes. Where needed, separate maps of the same quadrangles are published under such titles as "Economic Geology," "Surficial Geology," and "Engineering Geology." Each of these maps is issued both flat and folded.

Land-classification Maps show the present and potential agricultural use of land in public-land states. Each map is accompanied by a descriptive text showing the influence of the physical features on the use of the land for crop production, grazing, and other uses. Five maps, in 18 sheets, were published to the beginning of 1950.

The Geological Survey is making a series of standard topographic maps to cover the United States, Alaska, Hawaii, and Puerto Rico. The unit of survey is a quadrangle bounded by parallels of latitude and meridians of longitude, but different quadrangles are mapped on different scales, and consequently the standard maps, though of nearly uniform size (about 16½ by 20 inches), represent areas of different sizes. The published topographic maps now cover nearly half of the country. Each quadrangle is designated by the name of a city, town, or prominent natural feature within it. On the margins of the map are placed the names of adjoining quadrangles of which maps have been published. The maps are printed in three or more colors; contour lines are brown, water bodies are blue, man-made features (culture) are black, woodland areas are green, and main roads are red. In areas that have been covered by General Land Office surveys, township and section lines are shown. The United States Army grid system and the state rectangular coordinate systems are indicated on the margin of some maps.

Certain domestic topographic maps published by the Corps of Engineers (Department of the Army) and the Tennessee Valley Authority are also sold by the Geological Survey and included in its price lists.

Special topographic maps with descriptive text have been published for most of the national parks and some national monuments, national military parks, national historical parks, and Army camps. Nine sheets of the *International Map of the World on the scale of 1:1,000,000*, each covering 4 degrees of latitude and 6 degrees of longitude, have been issued by the Geological Survey to the beginning of 1950. A few miscellaneous topographic maps have also been published, including a small-scale map of the United States, 18 by 28 inches, on a scale of 1:7,000,000. Two relief maps on different scales are available.

A base map of the United States and one of Alaska have each been published on four different scales. Outline maps of the United States have been issued in two styles. *Physical Divisions of the United States* measures 28 by 31 inches and is on a scale of 1:7,000,000. The maps of the Tennessee River Basin include a base map and a hydraulic map, each on a scale of 1:500,000. River-survey Maps show the course and fall of streams, configuration of the valley floors and adjacent slopes, and cultural features. Most of them are in the West.

Maps of States. The U.S. Geological Survey has cooperated in the preparation and publication of geologic maps of many of the states. These are in process of changing rather rapidly, and the series ought to be of great importance in future years. Maps of Colorado (1935), Idaho (1947), Mississippi (1928), Montana (1945), New Mexico (1928), Oklahoma (1926), Texas (1937), and Wyoming (1925) are sold by the Geological Survey; the Oklahoma and Wyoming maps are at present (1950) out of print. The other maps, which are sold only by the individual states, are listed on page 203.

Oil and Gas Maps of California (1939), Kansas (1940), Louisiana (1939), Montana (preliminary, 1945), Oklahoma (1939), Texas (1938), and Wyoming (1946) have been published on a scale of 1:500,000.

The Missouri Basin Studies Maps include 20 maps of individual states in that region, showing various kinds of mineral deposits.

The Oil and Gas Preliminary Maps include four maps of three individual states: Colorado, Montana, and Wyoming.

Contour maps of Colorado, Connecticut, Massachusetts–Rhode Island, New Mexico, and Texas are available. Relief maps of Arizona, Idaho, Kentucky, Ohio, and Tennessee have also been published.

Base maps of every state have been issued on a scale of 1:500,000. Each state is also represented by a base map on a scale of 1:1,000,000.

Indexes and Catalogues. Index to Geologic Mapping in the United States is a series of state index maps showing by colored outlines the areas covered by published geologic maps. The key printed on each map gives the source of publication, scale, date, and authorship of each geologic map. The Geologic Map Indexes are prepared on scales of 1:750,000 and 1:1,000,000. Dated since 1947 they are available for purchase for most of the states.

Status of Topographic Mapping in the United States, Territories, and Possessions is an index map showing the extent and quality of the topographic and planimetric mapping by the Geological Survey and other Federal agencies. The third edition was issued in July 1947 and is distributed free; it is accompanied by text giving a detailed explanation of the map and its symbols.

Index Circulars show the areas covered by published topographic quad-

rangle maps and planimetric maps.   They have been issued for each state
or group of small states and for Alaska, Hawaii, and Puerto Rico and are
revised at frequent intervals.   Future Index Circulars will include maps
published by other Federal agencies as well as the Geological Survey.
Accompanying these Index Circulars, which are distributed free, is a separate report which lists publications of the Geological Survey that pertain
to each state, libraries where many of the publications may be consulted,
local dealers who sell topographic maps, and some miscellaneous information.

River-Survey Maps are indexed in *Water-Supply Paper* 995 and are
shown on the Index Circulars for the individual states.

A catalogue of these maps, indexes, and folios called "General Information on Maps and Folios Published by the Geological Survey" has been
reprinted from the general catalogue "Publications of the Geological Survey."   Occasional Geological Survey *Circulars* list preliminary maps that
have been distributed or prepared for open examination by the Geologic
Division and the Conservation Division.   Any of these catalogues may be
had free upon request.

The Geologic Folios and Topographic Sheets that were published by
the Geological Survey to 1931 are grouped by latitude and longitude in
"Geologic Index to the Publications of the United States Geological Survey," by George H. Albertson (see page 114).   The Cincinnati Public
Library maintains a card file by county of the topographic quadrangle maps
of the Geological Survey.

The Geological Survey maps, including folios and indexes, are sold by
the Chief of Distribution, Geological Survey, Washington.   Maps for areas
west of the Mississippi River are sold also by the Distribution Section,
Federal Center, Denver.   Prepayment is required, but stamps are not accepted.   A discount of 20 per cent is given on an order amounting to $10
or more, except certain maps offered at special prices.

Other Agencies

A total of 27 branches of the United States government are concerned
either directly or indirectly with the making of maps and charts.[1]   The
other agencies besides the Geological Survey that publish maps of particular
interest to geologists are the following.   Many other maps of a more
general interest are listed in "Official Map Publications" (see page 196)
and "Foreign Maps" (see page 196).

Bureau of Plant Industry, Soils, and Agricultural Engineering.
A series of colored Soil Survey Maps, showing the kinds of soil in each

[1] Brown, Lloyd A., "The Story of Maps," Little, Brown & Company, Boston,
1949.

county or other area surveyed, is published with descriptive text by the Bureau of Plant Industry, Soils, and Agricultural Engineering, Washington. These maps are listed in Price List 46 issued by the Superintendent of Documents, Washington.

Army Map Service. The Army Map Service of the Corps of Engineers, Department of the Army, Washington, has published a considerable number of topographic quadrangle maps which are sold in series. These cover part of the United States, as well as most of the rest of the world. Indexes to each series are sold at a low price; a list of these indexes is available on request to the commanding officer.

Coast and Geodetic Survey. Planimetric maps, without contours, compiled from air photographs taken of all districts adjacent to the Atlantic, Pacific, and Gulf of Mexico coasts of the United States since 1927 are sold by the Coast and Geodetic Survey, Washington (San Francisco, for California only; New Orleans, for the Gulf Coast; New York, for Cape Cod to Cape May). Some of the areas extend inland to include, for example, almost all of California. Index maps showing the area covered by each of these planimetric maps are issued free.

Geodetic Control Survey Index Maps are available for each of the states, showing horizontal and vertical controls.

Outline maps of the United States on five different projections and other maps are also sold by the Coast and Geodetic Survey.

Bureau of Land Management. A cloth geographic map of the United States and its territories and insular possessions, measuring 59 by 83 inches, on a scale of 1:2,500,000, was published by the General Land Office, Washington (which was consolidated with the Grazing Service into the Bureau of Land Management, July 16, 1946) and sold by the Superintendent of Documents, Washington. Another such map, 26 by 18 inches, on a scale of 1:5,000,000, and an outline map intermediate in size between these two are also available. Individual geographic maps of the 29 public-land states, Alaska, and Hawaii are issued by the same agency. These maps are all sold by the Superintendent of Documents, Washington.

Forest Service. Maps of many of the United States national forests are distributed free at regional offices and by the director, Forest Service, Washington.

National Park Service. Maps of most of the United States national parks are distributed free at regional offices and by the director, National Park Service, Washington or Chicago.

ORGANIZATION MAPS

Certain nationwide nonprofit organizations are important publishers of maps. These are included among the institutions whose bulletins are discussed in Chap. 11. All will furnish information about their maps upon request. The following such organizations are of particular significance as map publishers.

Geological Society of America, New York

Geological Map of North America, published in 1946 and now out of print, is of the greatest importance to geologists. It is in color and consists of two sheets, each 36 by 52 inches, on a scale of 1:5,000,000.

Glacial Map of North America, another important map, was published in 1946 in two sheets, measuring together 52 by 79 inches, on a scale of 1:4,500,000.

Geological Map of South America was published in 1945 in two sections on a scale of 1:5,000,000.

The same organization has for sale about 25 other colored geologic maps, most of them originally published in a *Memoir* or *Special Paper* or with an article in the *Bulletin of the Geological Society of America*. A list will be furnished upon request.

American Association of Petroleum Geologists, Tulsa

Tectonic Map of the United States is another major geologic map. It was prepared under the direction of the Committee on Tectonics, Division of Geology and Geography, National Research Council, and published in 1944 (3d printing, 1949). It is printed in seven colors on two sheets, each 40 by 50 inches, on a scale of 1:2,500,000.

Map of Cuba is also issued separately; the other maps published by this organization have appeared with articles in the *Bulletin of the American Association of Petroleum Geologists*.

American Geographical Society, New York

The World is a geographic map, prepared for the Department of State on a modified Mercator projection. It was published in 1947 and measures 35 by 57 inches, on a scale of 1:30,000,000. Topography and altitude are shown by form lines and layer tints, though the map may also be bought without layer tints.

Map of the Americas is a political-relief map in color, published in 1942 and 1948 in five sheets, each 35 by 46 inches, on a scale of 1:5,000,000.

Map of Hispanic America was compiled and reproduced in conformity with the *International Map of the World on the Scale of 1:1,000,000*. It was published from 1922 to 1945 in 107 sheets, each covering 4 degrees of latitude and 6 degrees of longitude. Topography is shown by contours and hypsometric tints.

Map of the Antarctic is a two-color map published in 1928 in four sheets, each 32 by 32 inches, on a scale of 1:4,000,000.

Outline Map Series includes five outline maps of North and South America.

Numerous maps originally published in the *Geographical Review*, most of them in color, and a few miscellaneous maps are also issued by the American Geographical Society. A catalogue will be sent free upon request.

National Geographic Society, New York

This organization publishes many colored maps covering all parts of the world. A catalogue will be sent free upon request.

STATE MAPS

The importance to the geologist of state bulletins, brought out in Chap. 12 of this book, is matched by that of state maps. The principal sources of these maps are state geologic surveys (see page 134); highway, railway, and public works departments; agricultural departments and experiment stations (see page 142); conservation and water departments; tax commissions; public-utility commissions; and planning boards.

The state geologic maps published by agencies of the Federal government have already been discussed (see page 199). Most of the state geologic surveys enumerated on pages 135 to 140 issue free price lists of their publications, and maps are usually given prominent attention. A description of the geologic, topographic, and planimetric mapping conducted by the state geologic surveys and names of the map series that they publish are given in "State Geological Surveys" by Wilson M. Laird, described on page 134.

The following state geologic maps are sold by the respective states and are available from the offices listed on pages 135 to 140. Those marked with an asterisk are also sold by the U. S. Geological Survey, which cooperated in the making of many of the rest of these maps.

Alabama	Minnesota
Arizona	*Mississippi
Arkansas	Missouri
California	New Jersey
Florida	New York
Georgia	Ohio
*Idaho	*Oklahoma
Illinois	Pennsylvania
Iowa	South Dakota
Kansas	Tennessee
Kentucky	Virginia
Louisiana	Washington
Maine	West Virginia
Maryland	Wisconsin
Michigan	

Other state geologic maps of the United States are listed in Section G, pp. 1332–1333, of "Directory of Geological Material in North America" by J. V. Howell and A. I. Levorsen, in *Bulletin of the American Association of Petroleum Geologists*, Vol. 30, No. 8, Pt. 2, August 1946.

State geographic, base, and outline maps published by agencies of the Federal government have already been discussed (see page 199). Some state maps are listed in the guides to state publications described on page 144. The most complete information, however, can be obtained direct from the issuing agencies. The names and addresses of various state agencies are given in *The Book of the States*, published biennially by the Council of State Governments, Chicago [8th ed., 1950–1951 (1950)]. Unpublished maps of state and other governmental subdivisions may usually be acquired by paying for their photographic reproduction.

COUNTY MAPS

Maps issued by counties are relatively more important than the printed publications discussed in Chap. 13. In addition to those actually reproduced for distribution, many more are prepared for the use of county agencies; copies may usually be obtained by photographing the original maps. The chief county officials whose offices make maps are the county surveyor, clerk, highway commissioner, and tax assessor. Worth-while information on county information is given on pages xvii and xviii of "The Official Publications of American Counties: A Union List, with an Introduction on the Collecting of County Publications" by James Goodwin Hodgson, Fort Collins, Colorado, 1937 (processed).

CITY MAPS

The engineering departments of numerous cities and towns have prepared special maps for various purposes, although few have been published. These may be examined and copied in the appropriate offices, along with privately made maps which have been filed in accordance with land-agency or fire-insurance regulations.

It must be mentioned in connection with these various political subdivisions of government that they are not necessarily coincidental with the area represented by any given series of maps. Thus, most county maps (except in Iowa) are produced by state agencies, and many of the kinds of state maps are made by the Federal government.

MAPS OF OTHER COUNTRIES

"Directory of Geologic Material in North America" (see page 208) contains detailed lists of the important geologic maps of Canada, Mexico, and the countries of Central America.

Chapters in "Official Map Publications" (see page 196) deal thoroughly with the government maps of Canada, Great Britain, and Germany. Summaries of government maps are given in Chap. 16 for Austria, Hungary, the Netherlands, and Norway. The 1936 status of topographic mapping in Latin America is discussed in Chap. 13. A list of international maps is also given.

"Foreign Maps" (see page 196) describes the characteristics of the maps of the chief mapping agencies of Canada and other countries, arranged alphabetically by country, and identifies the catalogues and lists that serve as guides to them.

Catalogues of maps issued by many nations are enumerated in "Government Document Bibliography in the United States and Elsewhere" by James B. Childs, Library of Congress, Washington (3d ed., 1942), and in various volumes of *Public Documents*, American Library Association, Chicago.

Canada

Most of the Canadian geologic maps have been prepared by the Geological Survey of Canada.

A major map is *Geological Map of the Dominion of Canada*, published in 1945 in two sections on a scale of 1:3,801,600.

Geologic and other maps are included among the other publications of the Geological Survey of Canada in Ferrier's "Annotated Catalogue of and Guide to the Publications of the Geological Survey of Canada, 1845–1917," described on page 151. A supplementary list, "Published Maps (1917–1934 inclusive)," compiled by P. J. Moran, was issued in 1934. The maps in the publications of the Geological Survey and the Bureau of Mines are indexed in "Cross-Index to the Maps and Illustrations of the Geological Survey and the Mines Branch (Bureau of Mines) of Canada, 1843–1946 (incl.)" by Carl Faessler, published in 1947 as *Géologie et Minéralogie contribution* 75 by Université Laval, Quebec. The maps are listed in three groups: (1) Non-Serial Maps, maps of the Geological Survey of Canada listed according to their publication numbers; (2) Geological Survey of Canada Serial Maps, maps of the Geological Survey of Canada forming the A series; and (3) Bureau of Mines Maps, maps of the Bureau of Mines (Mines Branch), Ottawa.

The geologic map of Alberta is sold by the province and is available from the following office: Alberta Department of Lands and Mines, Edmonton, Alberta. The geologic maps of British Columbia, Manitoba, New Brunswick, Nova Scotia, and Prince Edward Island, and those of parts of Ontario and Quebec have been published by the Geological Survey of Canada or some other branch of the Department of Mines and Resources.

Other provincial geologic maps of Canada are listed in Section G, pages 1332 to 1333, of the "Directory of Geological Material in North America" by J. V. Howell and A. I. Levorsen, in the *Bulletin of the American Association of Petroleum Geologists*, Vol. 30, No. 8, Pt. 2, August 1946.

Catalogues of maps of other countries

The map production of other countries besides Canada and the United States is discussed in the books mentioned on pages 204 to 205. Many of the individual maps are included in the lists of government documents enumerated and described in Chap. 14. They are also included in the following catalogues of geologic maps, published by the respective countries.

Argentina

"Catalogo de Mapas," Dirección de Minas y Geología, Ministerio de Agricultura de la Nación, Buenos Aires.

Germany

"Der Veröffentlichungen der Preussischen Geologischen," Landesanstalt, Berlin.
"Geologische Werke und Karten," Bayrisches Oberbergamt, Munich.
"Landkarten und sonstige Druckwerke," Württembergischen Statistischen Landesamts, Stuttgart.

Ireland

"List of Memoirs, Maps, Sections, etc., Published by the Geological Survey," Department of Industry and Commerce, Dublin.

Japan

"The Imperial Geological Survey of Japan: Its History, Organization, and Work," Imperial Geological Survey of Japan, Tokyo.

Netherlands

"Catalogus van Kaarten," Topographische Dienst, The Hague.
"Catalogus van Kaartwerken," N. V. J. Smulders, The Hague.

Additional information about foreign geologic maps may be obtained by writing to the geologic surveys listed in the directory on pages 162 to 168.

Two geologic maps of the world have been started, and one of them has been completed. *Geologische Karte der Erde* was published from 1929 to 1932 in 12 colored sheets, each 64 by 80 centimeters, on a scale of 1:15,-000,000. It was sponsored by the Preussische Geologische Landesanstalt, Berlin, and published by Gebrüder Borntraeger, Berlin. *Carte géologique internationale de la terre*, in 80 sheets on a scale of 1:5,000,000, was begun in 1932 under the sponsorship of the International Geological Congress.

Probably only 4 sheets were completed by the Preussische Geologische Landesanstalt, Berlin.

First Generalized Geologic Map of South America was published in 1945 on a scale of 1:11,200,000 as *Technical Paper* 2 by the United States Section of the Pan-American Institute of Mining Engineers and Geologists.

International Geological Map of Europe was published from 1881 to 1931. A second edition, to comprise 47 map sheets, on a scale of 1:1,500,000, was begun in 1932. It is sponsored by the International Geological Congress; about 8 sheets have been produced by the Preussische Geologische Landesanstalt, Berlin.

The geologic maps of North America and South America published by the Geological Society of America are described on page 202.

COMMERCIAL MAPS

The largest publishers of maps, at least in the United States, are commercial firms, publication being principally for advertising purposes. Besides the development of aerial photography, the most significant achievement in twentieth century cartography has been the tremendous free distribution by oil companies of accurate, up-to-date highway maps, which have made an entire nation more map conscious than it might otherwise have been. These and many other commercial maps are printed by a few map-engraving companies, which also sell individual maps and atlases under their own names. A review of some of the important "Publications of Large Commercial Map Firms" appeared in the October 1945 issue of *Subscription Books Bulletin* (Vol. 16, pp. 45–62).

Names and addresses of American and British commercial map manufacturers may be found in Section E of the "Directory of Geological Material in North America" by J. V. Howell and A. I. Levorsen, in the *Bulletin of the American Association of Petroleum Geologists*, Vol. 30, No. 8, Pt. 2, pp. 1330–1331, August 1946. Map manufacturers in the United States are listed in *Mac Rae's Blue Book*, published annually by Mac Rae's Blue Book Company, Chicago, and in *Thomas' Register of American Manufacturers*, published annually by Thomas Publishing Company, New York. Map publishers in Canada, Great Britain, South Africa, Australia, and Sweden are listed in *Kelly's Directory of Merchants, Manufacturers, and Shippers*, published by Kelly's Directories Ltd., London. The publishers of out-of-print maps that are stored in libraries are named in the card catalogue, wherever these are maintained for map entries.

AERIAL PHOTOGRAPHIC MAPS

Although aerial photographic maps are not true maps in conventional language, they serve many of the purposes of ordinary maps and are be-

+ are

coming the raw material for most of the finished maps of value to the geologist. The work of about nine government agencies and a number of commercial firms is now being coordinated in the Map Information Office of the U. S. Geological Survey, Washington. The fourth edition of the colored index map *Aerial Photography of the United States* was issued in June 1949 and may be obtained free upon request. It shows all areas known to have been photographed by or for Federal and state agencies and commercial firms, indicating the owner of the photographs. A circular, "Status of Aerial Photography of the United States," accompanies the map and gives valuable information on securing and selecting maps. To ascertain if aerial photographs of a specific area are available, a detailed description or a sketch of the area should be sent to the Map Information Office, which will advise from whom reproductions can be purchased.

The Map Information Office also distributes free a colored index map, *Aerial Mosaics of the United States,* the second edition of which was issued in September 1949. It is accompanied by a circular, "Status of Aerial Mosaics or Photo-Maps of the United States." Information pertaining to the availability and cost of aerial photography accomplished by units of the National Military Establishment may be obtained from the Air Adjutant General, Photographic Records and Services Division, Headquarters, United States Air Force, Washington.

Concise data on aerial photographs to 1946 are given for the political subdivisions of North America, including states of the United States and provinces of Canada, in the "Directory of Geological Material in North America" by J. V. Howell and A. I. Levorsen, in the *Bulletin of the American Association of Petroleum Geologists,* Vol. 30, No. 8, Pt. 2, August 1946.

DIRECTORY OF PUBLISHERS AND SERVICES

American Antiquarian Society, Worcester 5, Mass.

American Association of Museums, Old National Museum Building, Washington, D.C.

American Association of Petroleum Geologists, P. O. Box 979, Tulsa 1, Okla.

American Bureau of Metal Statistics, 50 Broadway, New York 4, N.Y.

American Chemical Society, Easton, Pa.; editorial office, Ohio State University, Columbus 10, Ohio.

American Council on Education, 744 Jackson Place, Washington 6, D.C.

American Documentation Institute, 1719 N Street, N.W., Washington 6, D.C.

American Geographical Society, Broadway at 156 Street, New York 32, N.Y.

American Geological Institute, 2101 Constitution Avenue, Washington 25, D.C.

American Geophysical Union, 5241 Broad Branch Road, N.W., Washington 15, D.C.

American Institute of Mining and Metallurgical Engineers, 29 West 39 Street, New York 18, N.Y.

American Library Association, 50 East Huron Street, Chicago 11, Ill.

American Metal Market, 18 Cliff Street, New York 7, N.Y.

American Petroleum Institute, 50 West 50 Street, New York, N.Y.

American Philosophical Society, Independence Square, Philadelphia 6, Pa.

Army Map Service, Corps of Engineers, 6500 Brooks Lane, Washington 16, D.C.

Edward Arnold and Company, 41 Maddox Street, Bond Street, London W.1, England.

Association of Geology Teachers, Department of Geology, Lawrence College, Appleton, Wis.

N. W. Ayer and Son, Inc., West Washington Square, Philadelphia 6, Pa.

Bituminous Coal Institute, 815 Southern Building, Washington 5, D.C.

R. R. Bowker Company, 62 West 45 Street, New York 19, N.Y.

British Information Services, 30 Rockefeller Plaza, New York 20, N.Y.

British Universities Encyclopaedia, Ltd., Bessemer House, Adelphi, London W.C.2, England.

Brookhaven National Laboratory, Upton, N.Y.

Bureau of Mines, Washington 25, D.C.; Publications Distribution Section, 4800 Forbes Street, Pittsburgh 13, Pa.

Cassell and Company, Ltd., 37 St. Andrew's Hall, Queen Victoria Street, London E.C.4, England.

Centre Nationale de la Recherche, 18 rue Pierre Curie, Paris 5, France.

Chemical Publishing Company, 26 Court Street, Brooklyn 2, N.Y.

Chemical Rubber Publishing Company, 2310 Superior Avenue, Cleveland, Ohio.

Colorado School of Mines, Golden, Colo.

Complete Service Publishing Company, 538 South Clark, Chicago, Ill.

Constable and Company, Ltd., 10 Orange Street, Leicester Square, London W.C.2, England.

Council of State Governments, 1313 East 60 Street, Chicago 37, Ill.

Current Publications, Ltd., 9 Duke Street, Toronto, Ontario, Canada.

Department of Agriculture Library, Room 1551 South Building, 14th and Independence Avenue, S.W., Washington 25, D.C.

Economic Geology Publishing Company, 100 Natural Resources Building, Urbana, Ill.

J. W. Edwards, Ann Arbor, Mich.

Edwards Bros., Inc., Ann Arbor, Mich.

Engineering Societies Library, 29 West 39 Street, New York 18, N.Y.

Europa Publications, Ltd., 56 Bloomsbury Street, London W.C.1, England.

F. W. Faxon Company, 83 Francis Street, Boston 15, Mass.

Foote Mineral Company, 500 Germantown Trust Company Building, Philadelphia 44, Pa.

Forest Press, Inc., Lake Placid Club, Essex County, New York.

French Embassy, Cultural Division, 934 Fifth Avenue, New York 21, N.Y.

Fuel Research Station, Greenwich, London S.E.10, England.

Geological Museum, Exhibition Road, South Kensington, London S.W.7, England.

Geological Society of America, 419 West 117 Street, New York, N.Y.

Geophysical Directory, 2124 Welch, Houston, Tex.

Government Printing Office, Washington 25, D.C.

Grafton and Company, 51 Great Russell Street, London W.C.1, England.

Charles Griffin and Company, Ltd., 42 Drury Lane, London W.C.2, England.

Gulf Publishing Company, P.O. Box 2608, Houston, Tex.

Handbook Publishers, Inc., Sandusky, Ohio.

Harper and Brothers, 49 East 33 Street, New York 16, N.Y.

His Majesty's Stationery Office, Adastral House, Kingsway, London W.C.2, England.

Houghton Mifflin Company, 2 Park Street, Boston 7, Mass.

Industrial Diamond Information Bureau, 32 Holburn Viaduct, London E.C.1, England.

Institute of Petroleum, Manson House, 26 Portland Place, London W.1, England.

Institution of Electrical Engineers, Savoy Place, London W.C.2, England.

International Microstat Corporation, 18 West 48 Street, New York 19, N.Y.

Kelly's Directories, Ltd., 186 Strand, London W.C.2, England.

Library Association, Stapley House, 33 Bloomsbury Square, London W.C.1, England.

Little, Brown and Company, Inc., 34 Beacon Street, Boston, Mass.

Longmans, Green and Company, Inc., 55 Fifth Avenue, New York 3, N.Y.

Maclean-Hunter Publishing Company, Ltd., 481 University Avenue, Toronto, Ontario, Canada.

Mac Rae's Blue Book Company, 18 East Huron Street, Chicago 11, Ill.

McGraw-Hill Book Company, Inc., 330 West 42 Street, New York 18, N.Y.

G. & C. Merriam Company, 47 Federal Street, Springfield 2, Mass.

Charles A. Meyer and Company, Inc., 25 Vanderbilt Avenue, New York 17, N.Y.

Midwest Oil Register, P.O. Box 892, Tulsa, Okla.

Mineral Book Company, Box 183, Colorado Springs, Colo.
Mineralogical Society, British Museum of Natural History, South Kensington, London S.W.7, England.
Mines Register, 425 West 25 Street, New York 1, N.Y.
Thomas Murby and Company, 40 Museum Street, London W.C.1, England.
Museums Association, Meteorological Buildings, Exhibition Road, London S.W.7, England.
National Academy of Sciences, 2101 Constitution Avenue, Washington 25, D.C.
National Business Publications, Gardenvale, Quebec, Canada.
National Geographic Society, Washington 6, D.C.
National Oil Scouts and Landmen's Association, Box 1095, Austin, Tex.
National Research Council, 2101 Constitution Avenue, Washington 25, D.C.
Thomas Nelson and Sons, 385 Madison Avenue, New York 17, N.Y.
New York Municipal Reference Library, 2230 Municipal Building, New York 7, N.Y.
New York Public Library, Fifth Avenue and 42 Street, New York 18, N.Y.
Northern Miner Press, Ltd., 122 Richmond West Street, Toronto, Ontario, Canada.
Office of Technical Services, Department of Commerce, Washington 25, D.C.
Oxford University Press, Press Road, Neasden, England.
Pan American Union, Washington 6, D.C.
Petroleum Publishers Inc., 1009 17 Street, Denver, Colo.
Petroleum Register, 412 West 6, Los Angeles, Calif.
Petroleum World, 412 West 6, Los Angeles, Calif.
Printers' Ink Publishing Company, Inc., 205 East 42 Street, New York 17, N.Y.
Publishers' Circular, Ltd., 171 High Street, Beckenham, Kent, England.
Recordak Corporation, 350 Madison Avenue, New York 17, N.Y.
Royal Geographical Society, Kensington Gore, London S.W.7, England.
Rutgers University Press, New Brunswick, New Jersey.
Saward's Journal, 15 Park Row, New York 7, N.Y.
Schoenhof's Foreign Books, Inc., 1280 Massachusetts Avenue, Cambridge 38, Mass.
Charles Scribner's Sons, 597 Fifth Avenue, New York 17, N.Y.
Walter E. Skinner, 20 Copthall Avenue, London E.C.2, England.
Peter Smith, 321 Fifth Avenue, New York 16, N.Y.
Smithsonian Institution, Washington 25, D.C.
Southwest Research Institute, 8500 Culebra Road, San Antonio, Tex.
Special Libraries Association, 31 East 10 Street, New York 3, N.Y.
Special Libraries and Information Bureaux, 52 Bloomsbury Street, London W.C.1, England.
Stechert-Hafner, Inc., 31 East 10 Street, New York 3, N.Y.
Superintendent of Documents, Government Printing Office, Washington 25, D.C.
Thomas Publishing Company, 461 Eighth Avenue, New York 1, N.Y.
Topographische Dienst, Prinsessegracht 15, The Hague, Netherlands.
United States National Museum, Smithsonian Institution, Washington 25, D.C
Universal Oil Products Company, 310 South Michigan, Chicago, Ill.

University of Chicago Press, 5750 Ellis Avenue, Chicago 37, Ill.
University of Illinois Library School, Room 328 Library, University of Illinois, Urbana, Ill.
University of Kentucky, Lexington, Ky.
University of New Mexico Press, University of New Mexico, Albuquerque, N.M.
University Microfilms, 313 North First Avenue, Ann Arbor, Mich.
D Van Nostrand Company, Inc., 250 Fourth Ave., New York 3, N.Y.
J. Whitaker and Sons, Ltd., 13 Bedford Square, London W.C.1, England.
John Wiley and Sons, Inc., 440 Fourth Avenue, New York 16, N.Y.
H. W. Wilson Company, 950 University Avenue, New York 52, N.Y.

INDEX

H